COVER: Anthony Devis, *Upton House from the South*
(slightly reduced in height)

UPTON HOUSE

The Bearsted Collection:
Pictures

THE NATIONAL TRUST
1964

UPTON HOUSE is 7 miles north-west of Banbury on the west side of the Stratford on Avon road (A.422). Particulars of Admission may be obtained from the National Trust.

Printed in England at The Curwen Press, Plaistow, E.13

Upton House

UPTON HOUSE stands just a little to the east of the crown of Edgehill Ridge and less than a mile to the south of the sham 'castle' built by Sanderson Miller—the eighteenth-century amateur architect and squire of Radway—to commemorate the spot where Charles I planted his standard before the pyrrhic victory of the royalist forces under Prince Rupert in 1642. Throughout Tudor times and until the Restoration the estate belonged to the Danvers family. In James II's reign it was owned by Sir Rushout Cullen, Bart., son of Sir Abraham Cullen, first Baronet, merchant of London. Sir Rushout proceeded to rebuild whatever house had previously existed at Upton.

Upon the death of Sir Rushout Cullen in 1730 the place was sold to Mr. William Bumstead, who carried out certain alterations. In 1757 Upton was bought by the rich banker, Francis Child, through whose grand-daughter it passed to the Earls of Jersey. In 1894 the seventh Earl of Jersey sold it and in 1927 the estate was acquired by the late and second Viscount Bearsted. Lord Bearsted in 1927–28 remodelled the house and developed the beautiful gardens under the direction of the late Morley Horder. In 1948, just before his death, he gave the house and grounds and his large collection of pictures and porcelain, with an endowment, to the Trust. Lord Bearsted's family continues to live at Upton.

The entrance, through stone piers and wrought iron screen, designed by Mr. Horder, and a straight avenue of Scots firs, planted by Francis Child, lead to the forecourt and north front of the house. In spite of subsequent alterations, both the north and south fronts of Upton preserve the core and express the character of James II's or William and Mary's reigns. The oldest rainwater heads bear Sir Rushout Cullen's initials and the date 1695, whereas the latest bear William Bumstead's initials, arms and the date 1735. The material used practically throughout is the local orange-golden stone, known as Hornton, and it has been suggested that Cullen's architect may have been Francis Smith, who rebuilt much of the town of Warwick after the fire of 1694 and some neighbouring country houses. Of the north front, the central block, with its baroque broken pediment, and the windows, with their bolection-moulded surrounds, mark Cullen's house, which Lord Bearsted carefully reinstated. The two receding wings are Horder's additions. On the south, or garden front, the Cullen building is defined by the quoined projections with hipped roofs. The adjacent wings, with the bays, were added in the early nineteenth century but remodelled, heightened and greatly improved by Morley Horder. On both fronts he succeeded in re-establishing order and symmetry.

Beyond the double terrace before the south front, stretches a wide lawn that appears to lead directly to a gently rising meadow. In fact between the lawn and meadow lies a steep coomb in which a series of herbaceous borders are ranged, separated by an old brick wall from the kitchen garden and a lake or formal canal at the bottom of it. The general layout of this steep garden may date from Sir Rushout Cullen's ownership. At the right-hand corner of the lawn a balustraded stairway, with retaining walls of dry stone revetting, descends the steep slope. To the west of this stairway and bounded by a high bank of cedars another coomb, at right angles to the first, forms a great amphitheatre, heavily wooded. In the hollow is a stewpond and at its head an attractive gardener's cottage of the same date as Sir Rushout Cullen's house. To the east of the formal canal the valley broadens out into yet another lake, formed by William Bumstead, with, on its far side, a classical temple built by Sanderson Miller.

Inside the central and old part of the house, the rooms have during the centuries been almost entirely altered. The entrance hall still retains a handsome stone chimney-piece of William Kent style and a beautiful staircase in the Inigo Jones tradition; but even the disposition of the last has been rearranged. Behind the hall, and occupying the centre of the south front, is the long gallery contrived by Mr. Horder. To the west of these two apartments are a series of modern galleries, almost entirely devoted to Lord Bearsted's works of art.

Very briefly they comprise a superb set of Brussels tapestries, known as the 'Hunts of Maximilian' after the cartoons by Bernard Van Orley: a collection of Sèvres porcelain and another of Chelsea figures: eighteenth-century English furniture, including a mahogany suite of settees and chairs covered with original gros point and petit point: and, above all, a collection of over one hundred and fifty pictures which are the subject of this catalogue.

J. L.-M.

THE PICTURES

This edition of the catalogue of the pictures belonging to the National Trust at Upton House is a revision of the one compiled by the 2nd Lord Bearsted and published by the Trust in 1950. The nature of the present publication is such that it is impossible for the compiler to acknowledge the assistance and advice received from a number of people. To Sir Anthony Blunt however a particular debt of gratitude must be expressed.

St.J.G.

ARRANGEMENT

The original, not always consecutive, numbers are retained and so also is the form of presentation whereby artists are listed in alphabetical order by schools. In order not to confuse the alphabetical sequence in a case where a picture has been re-ascribed, the position of the picture in the catalogue is transposed and a cross reference is provided from the original attribution. In Appendix I will be found a list of changed attributions (excluding instances of qualification of the name of an artist—i.e. 'School of', 'Follower of', etc.) and in Appendix II an index of artists appearing in the present catalogue.

DOCUMENTS

There are unfortunately no papers at Upton relating to the pictures. This will explain the absence in a number of cases of any information as to how a picture entered the collection.

MEASUREMENTS

Height precedes width. Panels are measured to their full extent; canvases as they are seen in their frames.

MEDIUM

Unless otherwise stated, oil, or in the case of early paintings, tempera, is implied.

DESCRIPTIONS

Right and left refers to the spectator's right and left unless the context implies the opposite.

ABBREVIATIONS

B.F.A.C.	Burlington Fine Arts Club.
B.I.	British Institution.
Friedländer	M. J. Friedländer, *Die Alt-niederländische Malerei*, vols. I–XIV, Berlin, 1924–37.
H. de Groot	C. Hofstede de Groot, *A Catalogue Raisonné of the Works of the most eminent Dutch Painters of the 17th Century*, vols. I–VIII, London, 1907–27; vols. IX and X, German edn., 1926, 1928.
R.A.	Royal Academy Summer Exhibitions.
R.A., Winter	Royal Academy Winter Exhibitions.
Smith	John Smith, *A Catalogue Raisonné of the Works of the most eminent Dutch, Flemish and French Painters*, vols. I–VIII and *Supplement*, 1829–42.
Upton catalogue	The 1950 catalogue of the pictures at Upton is referred to under this title.
Waagen	G. F. Waagen, *Treasures of Art in Great Britain*, vols. I–III, 1854, and supplementary volume, *Galleries and Cabinets of Art in Great Britain*, 1857.
Whitechapel	Whitechapel Art Gallery.
Whitechapel, 1955	Whitechapel Art Gallery, *Exhibition of Paintings from the Bearsted Collection*, 1955. (Note: at this exhibition ninety pictures from Upton, including four lent privately by Lord Bearsted, were shown. The catalogue, the work of the Gallery authorities, relied mainly upon the 1950 Upton catalogue. Only therefore in the few cases where it differs from the Upton catalogue is it referred to in the following text.)

PHOTOGRAPHS

All the pictures have been photographed by Blinkhorns, 5 South Bar, Banbury.

The Schools of Painting appear in the following order:

The British School

1 SIR WILLIAM BEECHEY, R.A., 1735–1839

Queen Charlotte

Canvas, $93\frac{1}{2} \times 56$ in.

COLL: probably Beechey sale, Foster's, 5 April 1835, lot 76 (the Queen in the garden at Frogmore, Windsor Castle in the distance): bt. by (?) Ryley—presumably bought in, for a similar portrait was included in the artist's sale at Christie's, 11 June 1836, lot 68: bought in. According to Roberts (*infra*) the same picture was passed at a sale at Rainy's, 19 July 1839, lot 43; Capt. T. A. Tatton sale (according to the sale catalogue having been acquired from the artist's family in 1879) Christie's, 14 December 1928, lot 37, repd.: bt. by Martin for Lord Bearsted.

LIT: W. Roberts, *Sir William Beechey*, London, 1907, pp. 42–43; W. G. Constable, 'English Painting in Lord Lee's Collection', *International Studio*, April 1930, p. 42.

EXH: Musée Moderne, Brussels, *Peinture Anglaise*, 1929, No. 2; R.A., Winter, *European Masters of the 18th Century*, 1954, No. 409.

RELATED PICTURES: (1) The original exhibited picture (omitted by Roberts, *op. cit.*) is in the Royal Collection at Buckingham Palace, a pendant to Beechey's portrait of *George III*. This differs from the present version in the substitution of Frogmore for Windsor in the background. (2) A version similar to the royal picture, said to have been presented by Queen Charlotte to her Lord Chamberlain, the 17th Earl of Morton, belonged to Lord Lee of Fareham (now at the Courtauld Institute of Art, London University). (3) The same picture was repeated as a half length and an example was formerly in the collection of W. Elkins of Philadelphia (repd. Roberts, *op. cit.*, p. 62). (4) Another was sold at the Parke-Bernet Galleries, New York, 30 March 1951, lot 248.

Walking to the right in a park, supposedly the garden at Frogmore, head turned towards the spectator, wearing a white muslin dress, straw hat with black lace veil and yellow stole falling over her shoulders; she is holding a puppy and a small spaniel runs in front of her; in the distance, right, the Round Tower of Windsor Castle. (Pentiment of spaniel's head.)

Charlotte Sophia of Mecklenburg-Strelitz (1744–1818), Queen Consort of George III. Beechey was appointed her portrait painter in 1793.

According to Roberts, who quotes the *Gentleman's Magazine* (April 1839, p. 433), Beechey painted a full length of the Queen in 1793 which was not exhibited until 1797 (R.A., No. 92), when it was shown together with the artist's portraits of five children of the Royal Family, now at Windsor. Roberts assumes that the portrait of the Queen was painted as a speculation, for it did not enter the Royal Collection, but remained on Beechey's hands and at the artist's sale in 1836 was described as 'Queen Charlotte in the garden at Frogmore, Windsor Castle in the distance. The original engraved picture.' Roberts is apparently referring here to the Upton version and is unaware of the Buckingham Palace portrait, which was in the Royal Collection by *c.* 1800 and was certainly the picture exhibited at the Academy in 1797. It was in fact this picture, with Frogmore in the background (and not Windsor), that was engraved by Ryder. Further confirmation that the portrait in the Royal Collection was the one exhibited in 1797 comes from a miniature copy of it by Henry Bone (now at Windsor) exhibited at the R.A., 1800, No. 575. This is said to be a copy of Beechey's exhibited picture and has inscribed on the back: 'After a picture painted in 1796 by Beechey.'

Assuming that the *Gentleman's Magazine* is correct in saying that Beechey painted a full-length portrait of Queen Charlotte in 1793, as he is likely to have done in the year that he was appointed court painter to the Queen, it is reasonable to suppose that it can be equated with the version now at Upton.

5 Attributed to LUKE CLENNELL, 1781–1840

A Village Fair

Canvas, $28 \times 39\frac{1}{2}$ in.

COLL: previous history and date of acquisition by Lord Bearsted unrecorded.

EXH: Laing Art Gallery, Newcastle-on-Tyne, *Festival of Britain*, 1951, No. 304.

The Bell Inn, left, with a group of figures, unsaddled horses, a hound and a man with a wheelbarrow; in the centre, beneath an oak tree, a shepherd and sheep; on the right two children are buying apples from a woman wearing a red cloak and blue skirt; beyond, on a village green, a horse fair is taking place.

Exhibited at Newcastle as by Clennell, but the attribution must be regarded as tentative. George Garrard is a possible author.

6 Attributed to JAMES COLE, active 1720–1743

A Flute Player

Canvas, 27¾ × 35½ in.

SIGNED: *I. Cole*

COLL: with Agnew, 1943, from whom acquired by Lord Bearsted.

LIT: *Illustrated London News*, CCII, 1943, p. 637, repd.; Clifford Smith, 'Flute Players of the 18th Century', *Country Life*, CXXII, 1956, p. 615.

A young man standing in the centre of a sparsely furnished panelled room, wearing a long red coat and black tricorne hat edged with gold, facing the spectator, about to play a flute. On the left a chair is placed by an open door through which another room is visible; on the right a table on which are some music scores stands against the wall beneath a bookcase; on the far wall hangs a French horn.

Perhaps by the engraver James Cole, although no paintings are known definitely to be by his hand. Strutt, *Biographical Dictionary of Engravers*, 1785, refers to him as 'a very indifferent engraver, employed principally by the booksellers and upon works of the commonest kind'. A bust-length portrait of Archdeacon Williams in the possession of the Society of Antiquaries, painted in the 1730's, bears a similar signature to No. 6.

Smith (*op. cit.*) writes that the German or transverse flute, here represented, was the most fashionable instrument in amateur musical circles at the time that this picture was painted, i.e. *c.* 1735. It replaced the original flute or recorder and was a novelty in the country at this date.

12 JOHN CONSTABLE, R.A., 1776–1837

A Suffolk Landscape, probably Dedham

Panel (Oak: ¼ in. fillet added all round, and additional ¼ in. at bottom). 7½ × 10⅞ in. (excluding additions).

COLL: a label on the back states that the picture was bought by Leggatt from Hugh Constable (grandson of the artist) in 1899 (Leggatt's pre-1923 archives have been destroyed); F. A. White sale, Christie's, 20 April 1934, lot 50, *A hot Day, Dedham*: bt. by Mrs. Douglas; date of acquisition by Lord Bearsted unrecorded.

A sketch showing a landscape with water meadows in the foreground and trees beyond, and, in the distance, rising ground. The view, if not at Dedham, is characteristic of Constable's Suffolk neighbourhood.

The centre and left of this scene appear to show the same piece of country as a drawing in the collection of the late Paul Oppé (exhibited R.A., Diploma Gallery, *The Paul Oppé Collection*, 1958, No. 178: *View near Dedham*).

13 NATHANIEL DANCE, R.A., 1735–1811

William Weddell and William Palgrave
(*Plate IIc*)

Canvas, 38¼ × 52¾ in.

SIGNED AND DATED: *N. Dance p Rome 1765*

COLL: painted for William Weddell; thence by descent in the family of his wife, Elizabeth Ramsden; Sir John Ramsden, 6th Bart., sale, Christie's, 27 May 1932, lot 58: bt. by Martin for Lord Bearsted.

LIT: Collins Baker and M. R. James, *British Painting*, London, 1933, Pl. 62.

EXH: Arts Council, touring, *Portrait Groups from National Trust Collections*, 1960, No. 20.

A scene in an Italian landscape with William Weddell, wearing red, seated under a tree in the centre with a dog at his feet; William Palgrave, in blue, stands conversing with him, his left arm resting on the back of Weddell's seat. The latter indicates a young servant (according to the Upton catalogue his name was Janson) who stands with his cap in his hand, right.

William Weddell was the second son of Richard Weddell, who bought Newby from the Blackett family. In 1766, on his return from the visit to Italy during which Dance's portrait was painted, Weddell commissioned Adam to enlarge Newby and to design a gallery for the sculpture he had acquired abroad. The collection, still in the house, is now owned by Captain Compton. In 1771 Weddell married Elizabeth, daughter of Sir John Ramsden, 3rd Bart. He was M.P. for Kingston-on-Hull from 1766–74 and for Malton Borough from 1775 until his death in 1792, when Newby passed to his great-nephew, Thomas, 3rd Lord Grantham, afterwards Earl de Grey. Busts of Weddell by Nollekens are at Newby and Ripon Minster, and a portrait by Batoni, painted in Italy in 1766, is at Newby.

The Rev. William Palgrave was the son of a physician at Ipswich. He was ordained deacon at Norwich in 1759, later becoming rector of Thrandeston and Palgrave in Suffolk. A friend of Thomas Gray's, the latter wrote to him when he was abroad in March 1765, advising him to keep a journal of the tour and suggesting a number of places he ought to visit on the way to Florence, 'where to be sure there is nothing worth seeing'. Palgrave also made a small collection of antiquities on this journey.

Dance was in Rome from 1754–65 and from 1760 onwards painted a number of groups of Englishmen on the Grand Tour.

14 RICHARD BARRETT DAVIS, 1782–1854

Thomas Sebright with the Fitzwilliam Hounds

Canvas, 28½ × 38¼ in.

SIGNED AND DATED: *R. B. Davis* 1839

COLL: possibly inherited by the 10th Lord Suffield with the Manor House, Swaffham, from Richard Hamond, son of Anthony Hamond of Westacre; sold by Lord Suffield to Leggatt, 1936, from whom it was acquired by Lord Bearsted.

ENGRAVED: by J. W. Giles, 1839 (lithograph: repd. as W. Sebright in *Squire Osbaldeston: his Autobiography*, ed. E. D. Cuming, 1926, p. 92).

He rides to the left, with the pack of hounds following him through a door in the wall leading to the kennels; the wall is bounded on the right by a small round tower with a pointed thatched roof, and the chimney stacks and castellated tower of a building are visible in the centre above some bushes which screen the wall.

Lord Fitzwilliam has kindly supplied the following information: Thomas Sebright (not William as previously stated) was huntsman to the Fitzwilliam from 1822–60 under the masterships of the 4th and 5th Earls and of the Hon. George Fitzwilliam. He came to this hunt from the famous sporting character Squire Osbaldeston, then master of the Quorn, whose letter of recommendation is preserved at Milton. Sebright, who had served as first whip with the Quorn, accompanied Osbaldeston when he took over the Hambledon for the season 1821–22 and he and Osbaldeston hunted the pack between them. An anonymous lithograph of *c.* 1850 shows Sebright as huntsman to the Fitzwilliam (repd. Cuming, *op. cit.*, p. 132).

The buildings in the background of the picture are the eighteenth-century kennels in the park at Milton, which were designed to look like a ruined castle. They are still in use today.

The picture has an indirect connection with Upton. In about 1760 Mr. Child, who then lived at Upton, sold the majority of his hounds to Lord Fitzwilliam. The pack shown with Sebright in Davis's portrait is probably therefore descended from Mr. Child's hounds.

14a ANTHONY DEVIS, 1729–1816

Upton House from the South

Canvas, 39⅜ × 49¼ in.

COLL: Francis Child of Upton; thence by family descent to the Earls of Jersey; Earl of Jersey Sale, Christie's, 15 July 1949, lot 132: bt. by the National Trust for Upton House.

A winter's day with the house seen from across the valley; four men are skating on the lake in the foreground and a horseman accompanied by some hounds is riding in the park beyond; fir-trees line either side of the lake and a small classical temple is at the far end.

Upton was bought in 1757 by the banker, Francis Child, through whose grand-daughter it passed to the Earls of Jersey, remaining in that family until sold by the 7th Earl in 1894. The steep coomb across which the house is seen in the picture now contains herbaceous borders and a formal canal.

At Lord Jersey's sale at Christie's in 1949 three other works by Anthony Devis were included (lots 129–131), another view of Upton and two of Osterley Park, a house which the Child family had acquired in 1711. The second Upton view was bought by Gooden and Fox; the other two pictures are now at Osterley.

15 Attributed to ARTHUR DEVIS, 1711–1787

(?) Francis Popham

Canvas, 35¾ × 49 in.

COLL: with Knoedler, 1922, whence acquired by Lord Bearsted; previous history unknown, but probably from the Leyborne-Popham family.

LIT: W. S. Sparrow, *British Sporting Artists*, London, 1922, p. 144, repd. (as by Stubbs); *idem, Angling in British Art*, London, 1923, p. 182, repd. (as by Stubbs or Arthur Devis).

EXH: 144 Piccadilly, London, *Sporting Pictures*, 1931, No. 13.

He is fishing in a stream in a garden, wearing a pale-mauve coat and red waistcoat, buff-coloured breeches and grey stockings, in the act of playing a fish; his hat, a box of flies, fish basket and two trout lie on the grass beside him; an overshot mill is in the left background, a plantation of trees beyond the garden fence, right, and a tree in the right foreground. (The composition suggests that the picture must at some time have been cut at the bottom.)

Formerly catalogued as a portrait of Edward William Leyborne-Popham, but as he was born in 1764, the approximate date of the present portrait, it must represent a man of the previous generation. Edward William Leyborne-Popham is almost certainly the sitter depicted by Arthur William Devis in No. 20 (cf. that picture).

If it is accepted that this is a member of the Popham family, which is probable in view of the traditional identification, the most likely candidate seems to be Francis Popham, who was the eldest son of Edward Popham (died 1779) and brother of Anne who married William Leyborne. It was the son of this latter marriage, Edward William, who on Francis Popham's death in 1780 succeeded his uncle to the Popham estates and later adopted the additional surname of Popham (cf. No. 20).

Francis Popham, who inherited from his father the properties of Hunstrete (Pensford, Somerset) and Littlecote (Ramsbury, Wiltshire) in 1779, died without issue the following year. He married Dorothy Hutton, daughter of the Archbishop of Canterbury. His younger brother Edward, who entered the Church, is unlikely to be the subject of the present portrait, which does not appear to represent a clergyman. (Gainsborough's portrait of a member of the Popham family—Bristol Art Gallery since 1956 and formerly in the Leyborne-Popham collection—was painted in the early 1760's and is wrongly inscribed *Edward Popham, M.P.* It represents a man belonging to the same generation as No. 15 and according to Waterhouse (*Gainsborough*, 1958, No. 438) may be William Leyborne, husband of Anne Popham.)

At Littlecote a branch of the Kennett 'passes through the garden and forms a preserve for trout' (Britton, *Beauties of Wiltshire*, 1825, vol. III, p. 259). It is possible that this is the scene depicted here.

While the attribution to Stubbs (cf. Sparrow, *op. cit.*) cannot be sustained, the attribution (Upton catalogue) to Devis is questionable: the figure is more naturally drawn and is less angular than is customary in his work. Mr. Pavière, author of *The Devis Family*, writes in a letter: 'I omitted this (picture) from my book as I do not feel, in spite of the landscape, that it is by Arthur Devis. Apart from the question of the age of the sitter (i.e. on the assumption that the sitter was Edward William Leyborne-Popham, born in 1764) he has a much squarer face than most of Arthur's figures.'

16 ARTHUR DEVIS, 1711–1787

The Edgar Children

Canvas, 33⅜ × 39½ in.

SIGNED AND DATED: *Art. Devis fe. 1762*

COLL: descended in the family of the younger child depicted here, who married General Hugonin. According to the Upton catalogue it remained with the family until 1929, when it was acquired by Lord Bearsted.

LIT: G. C. Williamson, *English Conversation Pieces*, London, 1931, p. 11, Pl. XXVII; S. H. Pavière, 'Biographical Notes on the Devis Family', *Walpole Society*, XXV, 1937, p. 124, No. 20; *idem, The Devis Family*, Leigh-on-Sea, 1950, p. 41, No. 36.

EXH: 25 Park Lane, London, *English Conversation Pieces*, 1930, No. 103; Arts Council, *English Conversation Pieces of the 18th Century*, 1946, No. 16; Whitechapel, 1955, No. 6 (Pl. VII in catalogue). It is possible that this is the picture entitled *Two Young Ladies with Grapes* which Devis exhibited at the Free Society of Artists in 1763 (No. 55).

Two little girls in pink frocks are standing facing each other on a terrace in the foreground, from which steps lead down to a park;

the elder holds a basket of grapes in one hand, a bunch of grapes in the other; the younger holds a peach in her hand, another in her apron; two small dogs accompany them.

Charlotte Edgar, born in 1757, the younger of the two children depicted here, married General François Lewis Hugonin, 4th Dragoons, of Nursted, near Petersfield. Their only surviving daughter, Charlotte, married Sir Roderick Murchison, President of the Royal Geographical Society.

17 ARTHUR DEVIS, 1711–1787

Mr. and Mrs. Van Harthals and their Son
(*Plate IId*)

Canvas, 34¾ × 46⅞ in.

SIGNED AND DATED: *Art. Devis. fe. 1749*

COLL: Miss Montague sale, Christie's, 29 June 1928, lot 55: bt. by Martin for Lord Bearsted.

LIT: W. T. Whitley, 'Conversation Pieces of the 18th Century', *The Collector*, IX, 1930, pp. 113, repd. 115; G. C. Williamson, *English Conversation Pieces*, London, 1931, Pl. XXII; S. H. Pavière, 'Arthur and Anthony Devis', *Antique Collector*, V, 1934, p. 42, repd.; *idem*, 'Biographical Notes on the Devis Family', *Walpole Society*, XXV, 1937, p. 122, No. 9; *idem, The Devis Family*, Leigh-on-Sea, 1950, p. 58, No. 137.

EXH: 25 Park Lane, London, *English Conversation Pieces*, 1930, No. 96 (Pl. XXII in catalogue); R.A., Winter, *British Art*, 1934, No. 336 (*Commemorative Catalogue*, No. 85); Arts Council, *English Conversation Pieces of the 18th Century*, 1946, No. 13; British Council (Hamburg, Oslo, Stockholm, Copenhagen), *British Painting from Hogarth to Turner*, 1949, No. 37; Arts Council, touring, *Portrait Groups from National Trust Collections*, 1960, No. 21.

A scene in a park with Mr. van Harthals at the right, wearing a brown coat and holding his hat in his hand, leaning against a tree-trunk; his wife in a white satin dress, a blue hat resting on her knees, is seated with a telescope by her side; their young son stands between them, wearing a green coat and breeches and pink waistcoat, leaning on a stick; a distant view of a winding river leading to the sea, with a church and buildings on a spit of land.

Whitley states that nothing appears to be known about the sitters except that the head of the family was a Dutch merchant who lived at Gravesend. The view in the background of the picture may therefore be intended to represent the Thames Estuary in that neighbourhood.

20 ARTHUR WILLIAM DEVIS, 1762–1822

Edward William Leyborne-Popham

Canvas, 29⅛ × 24⅛ in.

COLL: H. F. Leyborne-Popham, Hunstrete (according to Upton catalogue); with Tooth, 1945, and probably acquired by Lord Bearsted soon afterwards.

LIT: S. H. Pavière, *The Devis Family*, Leigh-on-Sea, 1950, p. 132, No. 111.

A young man seated to the left on a bank under a tree, looking towards the spectator, a fusil supported in his right hand, his legs crossed; he wears light infantry uniform consisting of red jacket with green facings, white breeches and black headdress with red plume.

Hitherto catalogued as 'A Member of the Leyborne-Popham Family'.

Mr. W. Y. Carman of the Imperial War Museum has provided the following information: The sitter is an officer wearing light infantry dress, which can be dated between 1784 and 1791. In view of the traditional title it is possible that the officer represented is Edward William Leyborne, who was a captain in the 24th Foot from 1788. This regiment wore green facings, silver lace and had their loops in pairs as in the present picture. The 24th Foot was posted to Canada in 1789, so there would have been a reason for having had the portrait painted before this date.

There seems every likelihood that this picture, which shows a young man aged about twenty, is a portrait painted in 1778–79 of Edward William Leyborne-Popham, who was born in 1764. The picture at Upton (No. 15) which was formerly said to depict this sitter shows a man who belongs to the previous generation.

Edward William Leyborne (1764–1843), son of William Leyborne (Governor in 1772 of Grenada, St. Vincent and Tobago) and Anne Popham, succeeded to the estates of Littlecote, Ramsbury, and Houndstrete (Hunstrete) Park, Pensford, on the death of his uncle, Francis Popham, in 1780 (cf. No. 15). In 1805 he assumed by royal licence the additional surname and arms of Popham. He rose to the rank of general; in 1806 he married Elizabeth, daughter of Archdeacon Andrew of Powderham, and left four sons and four daughters.

21 ENGLISH, early seventeenth century

A Lady of the Wenlock Family

Panel (Oak), 24⅜ × 18¼ in. (painted arched top).

INSCRIBED: *Aeta: XIIII*

COLL: anonymous sale, Christie's, 28 July 1926, lot 79, as by Zuccaro: bt. by Gooden and Fox; Lord Moyne sale, Christie's, 6 December 1946, lot 59: bt. by Arcade Gallery, whence acquired by Lord Bearsted.

LIT: D. Sutton, 'Elizabethan Portraiture', *Country Life*, CI, 1947, p. 1,007, repd.

EXH: Arcade Gallery, London, *Elizabethan Portraits*, 1947, No. 23.

A young girl, half length, facing slightly left, wearing a black dress, white lace cap and high ruff, lace collar and cuffs, holding a handkerchief in her left hand.

The title is taken from the catalogue entry in the sale at Christie's in 1926, followed in subsequent references. A portrait in the collection of the Duke of Buccleuch (*Catalogue of Pictures at Dalkeith*, 1911, No. 314), which bears a date of 1617, shows a lady wearing a similar cap and ruff.

22 ENGLISH, *c.* 1595

Sir John Cutts

Panel (Oak), 22½ × 17¾ in. (painted oval).

INSCRIBED: *To Sr John Cutts:*

In sea of thoughts that ebbe and flow, | Unmov'd, | My love to you is, let mee soe | Bee lov-d

COLL: anonymous sale, Christie's, 24 July 1936, lot 106: bt. by Freeman; date of acquisition by Lord Bearsted unrecorded.

A young man, head and shoulders, slightly left, wearing a white shirt with wide transparent lawn collar, his left hand resting on a scarlet sash which crosses his right shoulder. The inscription is illustrated by a view of waves dashing against a rock.

Formerly catalogued as a supposed portrait of Sir William Betts. Although the inscription has been strengthened there does not seem any particular reason to doubt its authenticity and the existence of another bust portrait showing the same man later in life confirms that it is a portrait of Sir John Cutts. This portrait, known through a photograph in the Witt Library, provenance unrecorded, is inscribed by the same

hand as No. 22, and the sitter's name is followed by a comparable couplet. In addition the date (1607) and age (35) are given. If this inscription is accepted, the sitter would have been born in 1672, and the present picture, which shows a youth in his early twenties, could be dated *c.* 1595.

It is possible that this is Sir John Cutts of Childerley, Cambridgeshire and Thaxted, Essex, whose monosyllabic name so offended the Spanish ambassador, whom Queen Elizabeth had consigned to his care. He married Anne Weld in 1632 and died in 1646.

60 ENGLISH, *c.* 1745

A Lady winding Wool and a Gentleman drawing

Canvas, 44⅞ × 37½ in.

COLL: said to have belonged to W. M. de Zoete; with Leggatt, 1928, from whom acquired by Lord Bearsted.

LIT: Sir Charles Holmes, 'Neglected English Masters', *Burlington Magazine*, LX, 1932, p. 302, Pl. 11d; Collins Baker and M. R. James, *British Painting*, London, 1933, p. 90; E. K. Waterhouse, 'English Conversation Pieces of the 18th Century', *Burlington Magazine*, LXXXVIII, 1946, p. 152; idem, *Painting in Britain*, London, 1953, p. 149.

EXH: B.F.A.C., *Neglected English Masters*, 1932, No. 135 (cf. W. T. Whitley's introduction to the catalogue, pp. 9–10); R. A., Winter, *British Art*, 1934, No. 266 (*Commemorative Catalogue*, No. 75, Pl. XXIII); Arts Council, *English Conversation Pieces of the 18th Century*, 1946, No. 9 (Pl. VIII in catalogue); Whitechapel, 1955, No. 4.

The interior of a carpeted room, with a view to a studio beyond. A lady sits left, at a table, winding wool on to a bobbin and wearing a white satin dress, pale blue coat edged with ermine, and lace cap. A man is seated, right, behind the table, wearing a navy-blue coat, white satin waistcoat with gold braid, white stock and cuffs, and holding a *porte-crayon*. A cat and two dogs are in the room.

Formerly attributed to Pond. Holmes considers it to be a work by this artist in an unusual phase, but the attribution is as uncertain as the identity of the sitters. Catalogued in the 1934 Exhibition as English, eighteenth century, and in the Arts Council Exhibition and elsewhere as by Pond, Waterhouse has suggested that it may be by Pieter van Bleeck, a Dutch painter who settled in England in 1723 and died in 1764 and who is known through a few theatrical groups and portraits. A suggestion that this may be a self-portrait of Pond (B.F.A.C. exhibition catalogue) does not seem to be supported when it is compared with Pond's etched self-portrait of 1751. A further connection with Pond, too tenuous to be entertained, has been inferred from the fact that the artist in the picture holds a crayon, a medium which Pond was among the first to make fashionable in England in the second quarter of the century. It has also been suggested that the lady may represent Peg Woffington (Holmes, *op. cit.*), but comparison with Pond's painting of c. 1758 of this lady (National Portrait Gallery, No. 650) reveals a superficial likeness only.

A date of c. 1745 has been generally accepted.

23 JOHN FERNELEY, 1781–1860

A Man in Hunt Uniform

Board, 14 × 12 in.

COLL: Lord Moyne (according to Upton catalogue); date of acquisition by Lord Bearsted unrecorded.

Standing full length in a landscape, facing the spectator, wearing pink coat and blue and white spotted stock, his crop held in his right hand, his cap in his left.

Formerly catalogued as a member of the Quorn, possibly a portrait of John Mytton.

24 THOMAS GAINSBOROUGH, R.A., 1727–1788

Crossing the Ford

Canvas, 12¾ × 14⅛ in.

COLL: Rev. H. Scott Trimmer (who may have inherited it from Gainsborough's Ipswich friend, Joshua Kirby); Trimmer sale, Christie's, 17 March 1860, lot 93: bt. by Rutley; G. Cavendish-Bentinck by 1890; his sale, Christie's, 11 July 1891, lot 551: bt. by M. Colnaghi; Mrs Martin Colnaghi sale, Robinson and Fisher, 20 November 1908, lot 183: bt. by Banks. Date of acquisition by Lord Bearsted unrecorded.

LIT: Sir W. Armstrong, *Gainsborough*, London 1898, p. 205; E. K. Waterhouse, *Gainsborough*, London, 1958, p. 111, No. 877.

EXH: R. A. Winter, 1890, No. 5; Guildhall, London, 1902, No. 67; Nottingham University, *Gainsborough*, 1962, No. 1.

A peasant is riding a donkey and driving a cow, calf and sheep across a stream; a second donkey is lying down at the left beneath a sandhill, over the brow of which is a thatched cottage among trees; water-meadows right, with the stream, crossed by a wooden bridge, winding into the distance.

The picture, which shows the influence of Wynants, belongs to Gainsborough's early Suffolk period and is dated by Waterhouse in the late 1740's. The scene has affinities with a landscape in the National Gallery of Scotland (No. 2,174), catalogued (1957) as a distant view of Cornard, and dated in the mid 1750's.

28 JAMES WILLIAM GILES, R.S.A., 1801–1870

A Falconer

Panel (Mahogany), 24 × 18⅛ in.

SIGNED AND DATED: *J. Giles S.A. 1833*

COLL: Duke of Leeds (information supplied in Upton catalogue). The ownership may be confirmed by an entry in a catalogue of the Duke of Leeds Collection (1902) in the possession of Professor Waterhouse. The entry reads *292. Falcon... Giles 1833*. The dimensions however are given as 36 × 27 in. Acquired by Lord Bearsted by 1937.

EXH: 39 Grosvenor Square, London, *British Country Life through the Centuries*, 1937, No. 365. (Giles exhibited 'A Sketch of a Falconer' at the Scottish Academy, 1835, No. 60, which may be this picture.)

He stands in a clearing among trees, wearing a uniform of long green coat and tall hat, with lures hung over his shoulder, a hooded peregrine on his gloved left hand and three others on blocks at the right. According to the Upton catalogue he was a falconer employed by the Duke of Leeds.

67 THOMAS HARDY, Exh. 1778–1798

William Augustus Bowles as an Indian Chief (*Plate Ic*)

Canvas, 29½ × 24½ in.

COLL: anonymous sale, Christie's, 19 July 1946, lot 110, as by Beechey: bt. by Baines. Date of acquisition by Lord Bearsted unrecorded.

EXH: R.A., 1791, No. 272; Whitechapel, 1955, No. 12.

ENGRAVED: by Joseph Grozer, 1791 (cf. Chaloner Smith, *British Mezzotint Portraits*, 1884, vol. II, pp. 604–5).

Half length, body turned to right, head facing; he wears a racoon skin cap with jewel and aigrette, an open white shirt with elbow bracelet, and a short bead scarf round his neck over which hangs a plain gorget.

Bowles was born in 1763, at an early age joined the British forces in America, was cashiered, took refuge with the Creek Indians, and from then on, as may be inferred from the unorthodox and romantic dress in which he chose to have his portrait painted, lived the life of an adventurer. He was reinstated in 1781 and in 1790 was in England with a party of Indians (according to the caption to the mezzotint he was 'Chief of the Embassy from the Creeke and Cherokee Nations'). It must have been at this time that he sat to Hardy. In 1791 he was back in America, occupied in trying to drive the Spaniards out of Florida. The next year he was captured and sent to Spain, ultimately escaping to Sierra Leone. In 1798 in England, in 1799 once again attacking the Spanish in Florida, he was captured a second time and was imprisoned at Havana, where he died in 1805.

Hitherto the picture has been attributed to Romney and it was alleged that the sitter was a British officer who may have accompanied one of the Indian chiefs when presented to George III in 1776. Professor Waterhouse, quoted in the catalogue of the Whitechapel Exhibition, suggested that the picture was painted in the 1790's, was not by Romney and showed clearly the influence of Lawrence. In fact the particular form of excise mark (with a crown and cipher), visible on the back of the unlined twill canvas, dates the picture after 1789.

35 GEORGE HENRY HARLOW, 1787–1819

'Mrs. Fitzwilliam'

Canvas, $15\frac{1}{2} \times 12\frac{1}{2}$ in. (oval).

COLL: previous history and date of acquisition by Lord Bearsted unrecorded.

Head and shoulders with dark hair, body turned slightly left, head slightly right, wearing a red dress.

Formerly catalogued without details or apparent foundation as a portrait of Mrs. Fitzwilliam. This may imply a portrait of the actress, Fanny Elizabeth Copeland (1801–54) who married the actor, Edward Fitzwilliam, in 1822, but she was 'light-complexioned' and in any case could not be represented if the attribution to Harlow (d. 1819), which seems plausible, is to be sustained.

38 FRANCIS HAYMAN, 1708–1776

Reputed Portrait of Hambleton Custance and Thomas Nuthall

Canvas, 30×25 in.

COLL: according to the Upton catalogue in the collection of A. H. Skinner, Sanderstead, Surrey; with Tooth in 1945, from whom acquired by Lord Bearsted.

LIT: Tate Gallery, *Report*, 1955–56, p. 18.

EXH: Whitechapel, 1955, No. 5; Iveagh Bequest, Kenwood, *Francis Hayman*, 1960, No. 13.

RELATED PICTURE: a portrait by Hayman of Custance and Nuthall, in an interior on their return from shooting, with affinities to the present picture but oblong instead of upright (25×30 in.) is in the Tate Gallery. (Another portrait of these sitters by Hayman is incorrectly described in the Upton catalogue as being in the Exeter Museum.)

A middle-aged man is seated at the left on a stone beneath a tree, a flask in his left hand, a staff leaning against his right shoulder, wearing a grey-brown coat, red waistcoat and black breeches; a younger man, walking to the left, wears a green coat and white waistcoat and carries a gun over the crook of his left arm, while with his right he gestures to his companion; a pointer looks up at him.

Hambleton Custance (1715–57), high sheriff of Norfolk in 1753, married Susannah Press. Their son was the 'Squire' of Parson Woodforde's *Diary*. Nuthall, who married Custance's widow in 1757, was solicitor to the East India Company and to the Treasury, and, until he lost favour in 1772, legal adviser to Lord Chatham. According to Walpole he embezzled £19,000. He died in 1775 after being shot by a highwayman on Hounslow Heath.

Formerly catalogued as a portrait of Custance and Nuthall, but it is unlikely that these sitters are represented. The double portrait in the

Tate (cf. *Related Picture*) came from the collection of Miss Nuthall, a descendant of the sitter, and has inscribed on the back the names and addresses of Custon (Weston House, Norwich) and Nuthall (New Lodge, Enfield, Middlesex) and their ages, 33 in both cases. The picture portrays the two men as being approximately the same age. They have both been shooting: one holds his gun, that of the other is leant against the wall in the background. On the basis of Custance's birth the picture would have been painted in 1748, which must be about the date of No. 38.

The Upton picture shows a young man carrying a gun and an older man seated, who has not been shooting and holds a stick. The resemblance to the figures in the Tate portrait, which it can be assumed in view of the provenance represent Custance and Nuthall, is more pronounced sartorially than it is physiognomically. A comparison with Gainsborough's portrait of Nuthall, whom he painted at Bath, 1760–64 (Waterhouse, *Gainsborough*, 1958, No. 526), is not helpful, but a portrait of Custance attributed to Ramsay, formerly at Weston House, clearly represents the young man seated on the left in the Tate picture.

39 JOHN FREDERICK HERRING, Senior, 1795–1865

Foxhunting Scenes: A set of eight

Canvas laid on board (circular, in one frame).

Nos. I–IV, $5\frac{1}{4}$ in. diam., Nos. V–VIII, $3\frac{1}{8}$ in. diam.

COLL: anonymous sale, Christie's, 26 May 1930, lot 75: bt. by Martin for Lord Bearsted.

EXH: Leamington Spa Art Gallery, *Art Treasures of Warwickshire*, 1948, No. 7; Whitechapel, *English Sporting Pictures*, 1950, No. 56.

COMPANION PICTURE: No. 40.

I. Huntsman and Hounds. II. Hunting in Covert. III. Full Cry. IV. The Kill. V. Earth Stopping at Night. VI. Three Hounds resting. VII. Hound in Landscape. VIII. Fox in Landscape.

40 JOHN FREDERICK HERRING, Senior, 1795–1865

Farmyard Scenes: A set of eight

Canvas laid on board (circular, in one frame).

Nos. I–IV, $5\frac{1}{4}$ in. diam., Nos. V–VIII, $3\frac{1}{8}$ in. diam.

COLL: anonymous sale, Christie's, 26 May 1930, lot 76: bt. by Martin for Lord Bearsted.

EXH: Whitechapel, *English Sporting Pictures*, 1950, No. 57.

COMPANION PICTURE: No. 39.

I. Pigs. II. Mare and Foal. III. Cows. IV. Sheep. V. Chickens. VI. Ducks. VII. Rabbits. VIII. Donkey.

41 JOSEPH HIGHMORE, 1692–1780

Isaac Welman

Canvas, $35\frac{1}{2} \times 27\frac{1}{2}$ in.

SIGNED AND DATED: *Jos. Highmore pin . . . 1737*

INSCRIBED: *Isaac Welman Esqre*

COLL: in the family possession until P. Welman sale, Christie's, 4 March 1927, lot 133: bt. by Colnaghi; included in two anonymous sales at Christie's, 10 May 1935, lot 30: bt. by Chance; 20 December 1935, lot 140: bt. by Ellis and Smith. Date of acquisition by Lord Bearsted unrecorded.

LIT: J. Scobell Armstrong, 'Highmore,' *Connoisseur*, LXXXVI, 1930, p. 219.

EXH: Secession Gallery, Vienna, *Meisterwerke Englischer Malerei*, 1927, No. 57 (repd. in catalogue).

COMPANION PICTURE: a portrait by Highmore of Simon Welman, younger brother of Isaac, was lot 29 in the Christie sale, 10 May 1935, and was with Spink in 1956.

As a young man, body facing, head turned half left, wearing a dark brown coat with gold frogging, scarlet waistcoat with gold braid, white lace cravat and cuffs; his right hand resting on a volume of Pope's *Works* on a table.

Isaac Welman (b. 1711) was the son of Simon Welman and Elizabeth Hawkins of Poundisford Park, Taunton. He married Jane, only daughter and heiress of Robert Tristram.

42 WILLIAM HOGARTH, 1697–1764

Gerard Anne Edwards in his Cradle

Canvas, $12\frac{1}{2} \times 15\frac{5}{8}$ in.

SIGNED: *W. Hogarth Pinxt*

COLL: by family descent to Col. W. F. N. Noel, who owned the picture when exhibited in 1912. Date of acquisition by Lord Bearsted unrecorded.

LIT: R. B. Beckett, *Hogarth*, London, 1949, p. 50, Pl. 64.

EXH: R.A., Winter, 1912, No. 151; Arts Council, Tate Gallery, *William Hogarth*, 1951, No. 31 (Pl. IV in catalogue); R.A., Winter, *European Masters of the 18th Century*, 1954, No. 44; Whitechapel, 1955, No. 1.

The child sits up in his cradle, looking to the right, holding a doll in a go-cart in his right hand; a dog is lying on the carpet, right.

Gerard Anne Edwards (1732–73) was the son of Lord Anne Hamilton (who took the name of Edwards) and the eccentric heiress, Mary Edwards of Kensington, who repudiated her marriage and had the child baptized as the son of a single woman. He was known as 'Handsome Edwards' and married Lady Jane Noel, daughter of the 4th Earl of Gainsborough.

The picture is dated by Beckett, on the basis of the child's age, late in 1732. The same toy is held by Gerard Anne Edwards in Hogarth's group of the Edwards family (Beckett, p. 42) in which the dog also appears. Beckett's suggestion that the dog is a later addition seems likely in view of its inferiority. The carpet also is poorly drawn and the signature is not very convincing. It is possible that No. 42 may be a fragment of a larger work, or may originally have been a sketch by Hogarth. In either case it could have been modified later to form a picture on its own account.

43 WILLIAM HOGARTH, 1697–1764

Morning (*Plate Id*)

Canvas, 29 × 24 in.

COLL: sold by Hogarth at a public auction in 1745 (cf. J. Nichols, *Biographical Anecdotes*, 1785, pp. 43–44) when it was bought by Sir William Heathcote; included in a MS. inventory of 1843 of the Heathcote pictures at Hursley Park as No. 11 in the South Drawing Room, with the note, *Cat of Pic in St James' Sqre 174(?)8*; Heathcote Heirlooms sale, Christie's, 27 May 1938, lot 29, repd.: bt. by Martin, with the companion, *Night*, for Lord Bearsted.

LIT: J. Nichols, *Biographical Anecdotes of Hogarth*, London, 1785, p. 211; J. Nichols and G. Steevens, *Genuine Works of Hogarth*, London, 1808, vol. II, p. 150 and vol. III, p. 174; J. Nichols, *Anecdotes of Hogarth*, London, 1833, p. 358; F. G. Stephens, *Catalogue of Prints and Drawings in the British Museum: Political and Personal Satires*, London, 1877, vol. III, Part 1, pp. 258–9; Austin Dobson, *Hogarth*, London, 1902, pp. 69, 172 (1907 edn., pp. 201–2); R. B. Beckett, *Hogarth*, London, 1949, p. 66, Pl. 89.

EXH: B.I., 1814, No. 181; R.A., Winter, 1885, No. 44; Huddersfield, *Two Hundred Years of British Painting*, 1946, No. 86; Whitechapel, *Five Centuries of European Painting*, 1948, No. 23; Arts Council, Tate Gallery, *Hogarth*, 1951, No. 38 (Pl. XII in catalogue); Whitechapel, 1955, No. 2.

ENGRAVED: by Hogarth (published 25 March 1738).

RELATED PICTURE: what was reputed to be an earlier version was sold in John Yates's sale at Sotheby's, 19 December 1827, lot 93, to Tayleur for £21. It was said to have been presented by Hogarth to his friend Mr. Birch (cf. Nichols, *Anecdotes*, 1833, p. 358).

COMPANION PICTURE: No. 44.

A scene in Covent Garden early on a winter's morning. In a group at the right outside Tom King's Coffee House two young men are making love to two market girls and two elderly women are crouched over a fire; one of these solicits alms from a lady, centre, on her way to St. Paul's Church accompanied by her foot-boy carrying a prayer book; in the background is a crowd of figures, some of whom are assembled round a quack on whose board is inscribed: *D. Miller's Famous . . .* (In the engraving this name is altered to *Dr. Rock*, a regular attendant at Covent Garden, but as seen in the picture the inscription may not be original.)

This and the companion picture, *Night*, form part of the series *The Four Times of Day*. The other two paintings in the series, *Noon* and *Evening* (collection, Earl of Ancaster) were bought by the 3rd Duke of Ancaster at Hogarth's auction in 1745. *Noon* is dated 1736. The set was reproduced by Hayman for the New Spring Gardens, Vauxhall (cf. L. Gowing, 'Hogarth, Hayman and the Vauxhall Decorations', *Burlington Magazine*, XCV, 1952, pp. 11–12: No. 3, *Morning*; No. 26, *Night*).

Nichols and Steevens (*Genuine Works*, vol. I, p. 103) relate that the 'old maid' was a friend or relative of Hogarth's and that he was struck from her will in consequence of this portrait. Fielding is said to have drawn upon this figure for the character of Bridget Allworthy in *Tom Jones* (cf. R. E. Moore, *Hogarth's Literary Relationships*, 1948, p. 127).

44 WILLIAM HOGARTH, 1697–1764

Night

Canvas, 29 × 24 in.

COLL: as No. 43 (No. 12 in Hursley Park inventory).

LIT: as No. 43 (repd. as Pl. 92 in Beckett).

EXH: B.I., 1814, No. 191; R.A., Winter, 1885, No. 48; Whitechapel, *Five Centuries of European Painting*, 1948, No. 23; Arts Council, Tate Gallery, *Hogarth*, 1951, No. 39; Whitechapel, 1955, No. 3.

ENGRAVED: as No. 43.

COMPANION PICTURE: No. 43.

A moonlight scene in a narrow lane leading from Whitehall to Charing Cross, with the Rummer Tavern ('The New Bagnio') on one side, the Cardigan's Head on the other and the equestrian statue of Charles I in the distance. Bonfires have been lit in celebration of Restoration Day and the Salisbury Flying Coach has upset over one of them. Left, two men, one of whom fires off a pistol, stand watching the efforts of the passengers to extricate themselves. In the foreground towards the right a freemason is supported home; further to the right the interior of a barber-surgeon's is seen through a window; figures are huddled asleep beneath the sill and in the background a man is filling a vat from a barrel.

The identification of the freemason with Sir Thomas (de) Veil, a severe successor to Horace Walpole as Inspector General of Imports and Exports, is questionable (cf. Nichols and Steevens, *Genuine Works*, vol. 11, p. 150, where reference is also made to the overturn of the Salisbury Coach implying a satire on the inventor of that type of coach).

45 JOHN HOPPNER, R.A., 1758–1810

The Marquise de Sivrac and her Son

Canvas, 34½ × 31½ in.

COLL: Mrs. Stephens of Belgrave Rectory, Leicester, niece of the sitter; in 1898 sold by her daughter to Agnew, from whom it was acquired by G. Harland Peck; his sale, Christie's, 25 June 1920, lot 83: bt. by Davis; date of acquisition by Lord Bearsted unrecorded.

LIT: J. Frankau, 'Mr. Harland Peck's Collection', *Connoisseur*, V, 1903, Pl. 91, repd.; W. McKay and W. Roberts, *Hoppner*, London, 1909, p. 232.

Half lengths in a landscape; she wears a pale turquoise dress with white muslin fichu, her powdered hair bound by a ribbon; her arm is round the shoulder of a small boy, who stands beside her, right, wearing a maroon velvet coat and white lace collar.

The unusual dimensions of the canvas and the awkwardness of the composition, together with a possible alteration to the position of the woman's badly damaged and now repainted right arm, suggest that the picture may have been cut down from a 50 × 40 in. canvas. The existence of a portrait by Hoppner of the Marquis de Sivrac (sold at Christie's, 24 February 1912, lot 108), size 35 × 31 in., which may be a companion to No. 45, need not necessarily imply that this assumption is wrong since it also could have been reduced.

The sitters are referred to as the Marquise de Séverac (*née* Bonar) and her son in the Upton catalogue and by Ward and Roberts as Sivrac. The Bonar reference is to Thomson Bonar (born *c.* 1740), described as a Paris banker and a Russian merchant, who lived at Camden Place, Chislehurst and with his wife was murdered by a footman in 1812. His daughter married Charles, Marquis de Sivrac of Rieux; both their children died young. It was the daughter of de Sivrac's brother who married the Rev. Richard Stephens and in whose family the portrait remained until 1898.

47 GEORGE HENRY LAPORTE, d. 1873

The 13th Earl of Eglinton on Horseback

Canvas, 27 × 35⅜ in.

COLL: previous history and date of acquisition by Lord Bearsted unrecorded.

He is riding to the left, wearing a pink coat and turning to face the spectator, on a dark bay hunter; beyond him on the left are two hunt servants with hounds; in the distance, right, stands a house.

According to the Upton catalogue the house is Sandford Hall, Shropshire, and the horse ridden by Lord Eglinton is 'Emerald'. (On the back of the unlined canvas is written 'Emerald by Grafton'.)

There are two Sandford Halls in Shropshire, one a Victorianized house at Prees (until lately the home of the Sandford family), the other at

West Felton (owned *c*. 1850 by Samuel Bickerton and prior to that by the Tyrwhitt family). It is not clear which, if either, of these houses is shown. The area is noted for hunting and it is possible that Lord Eglinton leased one or other of the properties as a hunting box.

Judging by the age of the sitter the picture was probably painted *c*. 1840–50 (Lord Eglinton was born in 1812; for biography see No. 64, the Raeburn portrait of him as a child, in which he is depicted in the same attitude as in No. 47).

48 SIR THOMAS LAWRENCE, P.R.A., 1769–1830

William IV as Duke of Clarence

Canvas, $49\frac{1}{2} \times 39\frac{1}{2}$ in.

COLL: first noted in the collection of Baroness Burdett-Coutts (d. 1881), daughter and co-heir of Sir Francis Burdett, Bart., of Ramsbury; in the sale of her husband, W. Burdett-Coutts, Christie's, 4 May 1922, lot 42, repd.: bt. by Davis. Acquired by Lord Bearsted in 1937.

LIT: Sir W. Armstrong, *Lawrence*, London, 1913, p. 171; K. Garlick, *Lawrence*, London, 1954, p. 32.

EXH: Agnew, London, *Portraits of Kings and Queens of England*, 1935, No. 66; R.A., Diploma Gallery, *Kings and Queens*, 1953, No. 265; Whitechapel, 1955, No. 19.

RELATED PICTURE: at Penshurst (see below).

Three-quarter length, standing, facing, head turned to right, in blue coat, white waistcoat and stock, grey breeches and powdered hair; he wears the star of the garter and holds a hat in his right hand and a stick in his gloved left; cliffs and seascape background and setting sun.

The Duke of Clarence (1765–1837), third son of George IV, succeeded to the throne as William IV in 1830.

Dated by Armstrong, 1790–95, and referred to by Garlick as a replica of the portrait in the collection of Lord De L'Isle and Dudley at Penshurst, which he regards as possibly being the picture exhibited at the Academy in 1793, No. 63. 'The type is reminiscent of a half-length drawing of the Duke by Lawrence after a bust by Lock (engraved by E. Scott, 1788)'—Oliver Millar, catalogue entry, R.A. Exhibition, 1953. No. 48 is characteristic of Lawrence's early work and is certainly autograph.

49 RICHARD LIVESAY, d. (?)1823

The Duchess of York presented to George III

Canvas, $37\frac{3}{4} \times 49\frac{1}{2}$ in.

INSCRIBED (by the artist?) on the stretcher: *No. 1 Introduction of Duchess of York to the Royal Family*

COLL: No. 49, which was included in the Fuller Maitland sale (Christie's, 14 July 1922, lot 127, as by Livesay), is referred back in the auctioneer's copy of the catalogue to an anonymous sale ('A Gentleman in the North') at Christie's, 17 February 1849, lot 94, when it was catalogued as by Copley and bought by Daniel. However, a picture exactly answering the description of No. 49 (size not given) appeared in an even earlier anonymous sale at Christie's, 23 June 1838, lot 119 (buyer's name not recorded). It was catalogued as by West and Livesay, with the information that it had been painted for George III and came from the collection of Queen Charlotte. Whether or not this is the present picture there is no evidence, according to Oliver Millar, that it was ever in the Royal Collection. In 1922 No. 49 was bought by Levy; the date of its acquisition by Lord Bearsted is not recorded.

EXH: Arts Council, *English Conversation Pieces of the 18th Century*, 1946, No. 30.

ENGRAVED: by J. Murphy, 1793.

Frederica, eldest daughter of Frederick William II, King of Prussia, is being presented by Queen Charlotte to George III, on the occasion of her marriage to Frederick, Duke of York, the King's second son, in 1791. The event takes place on a terrace, with the King and Queen standing in the centre, the latter holding by the hand the young princess who curtsies before the king; behind, the Prince of Wales, and right, the Duke of Clarence; the Duke of York advancing from the right is sponsoring the introduction. On the left, behind the King, are the Princess Royal and Princesses Augusta, Elizabeth, Mary, Sophia and Amelia.

The inscription on the *verso* implies that the picture may belong to a series. In fact Redgrave (*Dictionary of Artists*, 1878) mentions what at first sight could be a companion picture, a group of George III with his Queen and family, to whom the Duchess of Gloucester is being introduced. For reasons of date any relationship, if Redgrave is not mistaken in the subject, appears improbable.

Livesay, who assisted West, moved to

Windsor in 1790 when he became drawing master to the Royal Family.

50 BEN MARSHALL, 1767–1835

Francis Dukinfield Astley and his Harriers
(*Plate IIb*)

Canvas, $39\frac{1}{8} \times 49$ in.

SIGNED AND DATED: *B. Marshall pt. 1809*

COLL: Dukinfield Astley, for whom the picture was painted; thence by family descent to Sir Arthur Nicholson; his sale, Christie's, 14 May 1926, lot 82, repd.: bt. by Knoedler, from whom acquired by Lord Bearsted.

LIT: H. A. Bryden, 'Pictures of Old English Sport', *Country Life*, LXIII, 1928, pp. 893, repd. 894; W. S. Sparrow, *George Stubbs and Ben Marshall*, London, 1929, p. 53; Collins Baker and M. R. James, *British Painting*, London, 1933, pp. 144 (note), 145; W. Gaunt, *British Painting from Hogarth's Day to Ours*, London, 1945, Pl. 7.

EXH: Knoedler, London, *Old Sporting Pictures*, 1928, No. 19; Musée Moderne, Brussels, *Peinture Anglaise*, 1929, No. 108; R.A., Winter, *British Art*, 1934, No. 417 (*Commemorative Catalogue*, No. 320, Pl. XCI); Louvre, Paris, *Peinture Anglaise*, 1938, No. 19.

ENGRAVED: by R. Woodman, 1809; F. C. Dixon (mezzotint).

A landscape in Cheshire, with the building known as the Hunter's Tower on the horizon of an extensive view. On the right Dukinfield Astley, in scarlet on a bay horse, raising his hat: further back, riding to left, a horseman wearing a black coat, said to be Mr. Abel Wood, with two hunt servants; in the foreground, hounds and the terrier.

Francis Dukinfield Astley (1781–1825) of Dukinfield Hall, Cheshire, was sheriff of Cheshire, 1806–7. He was a man of literary talents and in 1819 published *Poems and Translations*. He kept his own pack of harriers, and built the Hunter's Tower, on a hill overlooking Stalybridge, in 1807. In 1812 he married Susan Palmer; there were two sons of the marriage.

51 BEN MARSHALL, 1767–1835

A Farmer with a Horse and Cart

Canvas, $27\frac{1}{8} \times 35\frac{1}{4}$ in.

SIGNED AND DATED (as inscription on the waggon): *Farmer Marshall, '09*

COLL: previous history and date of acquisition by Lord Bearsted unrecorded, but at Upton by 1937.

EXH: 39 Grosvenor Square, London, *British Country Life through the Centuries*, 1937, No. 266; British Council (Hamburg, Oslo, Stockholm, Copenhagen), *British Painting from Hogarth to Turner*, 1949, No. 69.

A carter holds up the shafts of a farm waggon, to which he is about to harness a shire horse; in the background, left, two Suffolk Punches are drawing a plough.

The Upton catalogue records Sir Anthony Blunt's suggestion that this may be a copy by Géricault during his stay in England. In the absence of more positive evidence and the presence of an acceptable signature the attribution to Marshall is retained here. The picture is coarsely but thinly painted on twill canvas, in the rather dry technique characteristic of Marshall.

53 GEORGE MORLAND, 1763–1804

The Departure

Canvas, $14\frac{3}{4} \times 12$ in.

SIGNED AND DATED: *G. Morland, 1792*

COLL: R. Manley Foster Sale, Christie's, 17 June 1927, lot 39: bt. by Pearce; date of acquisition by Lord Bearsted unrecorded.

EXH: Arts Council, *English Conversation Pieces of the 18th Century*, 1946, No. 29; Arts Council, Tate Gallery, *George Morland*, 1954, No. 19.

A winter scene: at a cottage door a youth takes leave of a girl, whose right hand he holds; a coachman stands by their side; the coach is seen in the background.

The figures adopt the same attitudes and the composition is similar to the small canvas entitled *The Soldier's Farewell* (1789) in the Lady Lever Art Gallery, Port Sunlight.

54 JOHN HAMILTON MORTIMER, A.R.A., 1741–1779

The Rev. Charles Everard and two Others playing Billiards

Canvas, $39\frac{1}{4} \times 48$ in.

COLL: descended in the Booth family, Twemlow Hall, until 1862, when the house and contents were bought by Col. Egerton Leigh.

A label attached to the back of the picture, signed 'E.L. 1893' records that it was bequeathed to William Charles Booth in 1829 and 'sold to us with the house and property 1862'. It was acquired from this family sometime before 1930 by Lord Bearsted.

LIT: G. C. Williamson, *English Conversation Pieces of the 18th Century*, London, 1931, p. 23, Pl. LXVII; Collins Baker and M. R. James, *British Painting*, London, 1933, p. 138.

EXH: 25 Park Lane, London, *English Conversation Pieces*, 1930, No. 21; R.A., Winter, *British Art*, 1934, No. 409 (*Commemorative Catalogue*, No. 257, Pl. LXXVII); 39 Grosvenor Square, London, *British Country Life through the Centuries*, 1937, No. 295A; Arts Council, *English Conversation Pieces of the 18th Century*, 1946, No. 23 (Pl. III in catalogue); Whitechapel, 1955, No. 15 (Pl. VI in catalogue); Arts Council, touring, *Portrait Groups from National Trust Collections*, 1960, No. 22.

The interior of a classical room with, left, the Rev. Charles Everard (Booth) in dark clothes, seated holding a mace in his left hand and resting his right arm on the back of a chair; next to him stands a younger man who leans against the billiard table, his legs crossed, a mace in his left hand, turning towards a man who stands at the right, in shirtsleeves and blue waistcoat.

The Rev. Charles Everard (d. 1792), Prebendary of York and Sarum, was the elder son of the Rev. Charles Everard and Mary, daughter of Lawrence Booth of Twemlow, Cheshire. In 1786 he succeeded his uncle to Twemlow and assumed the name and arms of Booth. He married, but died without issue and was succeeded by his nephew Capt. Walter Griffith, R.N., who also assumed the name of Booth on inheriting Twemlow. He in turn was succeeded by his kinsman, William Charles Booth (formerly Bache), whose son sold Twemlow.

In the Upton catalogue the figure in the centre is described as William Charles, son of Charles Everard, but in the latter's will no reference is made to any children and it is possible that this man is Capt. Walter Griffith. The identity of the third figure is untraced.

The scene depicted might be identifiable if more was known about the Rev. Charles Everard. If by Mortimer, which is not in doubt, the picture must have been painted towards the end of his life. As he died in 1779, and Charles Everard did not inherit Twemlow until 1786, it is probably unlikely that the billiard room represented here is at Twemlow, as has been suggested.

The players are seen using the mace, which was superseded by the cue soon after 1800.

55 ALEXANDER NASMYTH, 1758–1840

The 7th Baron Belhaven

Canvas, $44\frac{1}{8} \times 33\frac{1}{8}$ in.

COLL: P. D. Stange sale, Christie's, 16 May 1919, lot 26: bt. by Lord Bearsted.

Standing, right, in a Scottish landscape, wearing a short red coat, buff-coloured breeches and riding boots, leaning his right arm against a tree, legs crossed, holding in his left hand his hat and crop; a dog looks up at him; in the middle distance a groom with two horses and dogs, and beyond, a house on a hill across a valley.

William, 7th Lord Belhaven and Stenton (1765–1814), son of Robert Hamilton of Wishaw, presented a petition to George III claiming the peerage under a clause in the 1675 patent, which was admitted by the House of Lords in 1799. In 1789 he married Penelope, daughter of Ranald Macdonald of Clanranald (grandfather of the children in the Raeburn portrait, No. 63 in the collection).

Lord Belhaven, in whose family collection the portrait is not recorded, has kindly supplied the following information: the house in the background is almost certainly Wishaw in Lanarkshire, which has recently been demolished. There is an indication that beyond the horseman is a river, which must be the South Calder Water. By 1950 the trees below the house had grown to such an extent that they threatened to pull down the house and glen.

The portrait must have been executed before William Hamilton acquired the title. It shows a young man who can hardly be more than twenty-five years old and it may therefore have been painted on the occasion either of his twenty-first birthday or of his marriage: i.e. *c.* 1786–89.

56 JOHN OPIE, R.A., 1761–1807

A Country Girl

Canvas, $49\frac{1}{2} \times 39\frac{3}{8}$ in.

COLL: no provenance given in monographs quoted below, but in the collection of the Marquess of Ripon (according to 1914 sale catalogue) and of Sir Hugh Lane (according to Upton catalogue); Lady Young sale, Christie's, 6 May 1905, lot 120: bt. by Samuel; Arthur Grenfell sale, Christie's, 26 June 1914, lot 51: bt. by Huggins. Date of acquisition by Lord Bearsted unrecorded.

LIT: J. J. Rogers, *Opie and his Works*, London, 1878, p. 207; A. Earland, *John Opie and his Circle*, London, 1911, p. 343.

EXH: R.A., 1795, No. 124.

Full length, seated on a bank to left, looking slightly right; she wears a brown dress with short white sleeves and holds a basket on her left arm.

It appears that the same model was used here as for the girl in the *Blind Beggar of Bethnal Green* (Ashmolean, Oxford) and the same rather broad and summary technique is employed in both paintings. While the Ashmolean picture is dated by Earland (*op. cit.*, p. 339) after 1782, it is likely to be nearer 1795, the year in which No. 56 was exhibited and, it can be inferred, painted.

Earland quotes the *Morning Chronicle* for 13 May 1795, criticizing the two pictures sent by Opie to the Academy that year. The present picture is less severely castigated than the one which accompanied it and is described as being 'properly enough formed of Nature's coarsest clay'.

57 RICHARD MORTON PAYE,
active 1773–1821

The Artist in his Studio

Canvas, $28\frac{7}{8} \times 23\frac{3}{4}$ in.

COLL: Sir John Neeld, 1889; L. W. Neeld sale, Christie's, 13 July 1945, lot 141: bt. by Chance (for Lord Bearsted?).

LIT: E. W. Clayton, 'Richard Morton Paye', *Connoisseur*, XXXVII, 1913, p. 236.

EXH: Society of Artists, 1783, No. 203; Grosvenor Galleries, London, 1889, No. 131.

As a young man, seated by candlelight in a studio; he faces right, his head turned towards the spectator, an etching point in his right hand, a copper plate and a small canvas which he is copying supported on the table in front of him; behind is a gilt mirror in which the candle is reflected; a cast of the Apollo Belvedere is in the corner of the room.

The picture exhibited in 1783 was entitled *An Engraver at Work*, but in the article on Paye in the *Dictionary of National Biography* it is alluded to as a self portrait. Clayton refers to the present picture as a self portrait. That it is also one and the same as the picture exhibited in 1783 seems highly probable in view of the fact that the artist is seen to be copying a reduced version of the portrait by Dance of Percival Pott, F.R.S. (now Royal College of Surgeons), which Paye engraved and published in 1783.

59 MATTHEW WILLIAM PETERS,
1742–1814

Three Children dressing up

Canvas, $54\frac{1}{2} \times 39\frac{1}{4}$ in.

COLL: said to have belonged to the artist, Ramsay Richard Reinagle, and thence by family descent to Charles W. Bedwell, whose mother was a Reinagle; C. W. Bedwell sale, Christie's, 23 July 1920, lot 128: bt. by Reeves; date of acquisition by Lord Bearsted unrecorded. (According to the article in the *Connoisseur* (*infra*) the canvas had been rolled up and was not rediscovered until 1903.)

LIT: anon. article, 'A Portrait Group by the Rev. M. W. Peters', *Connoisseur*, LVIII, 1920, p. 240, repd. p. 187; Collins Baker and M. R. James, *British Painting*, London, 1933, p. 128.

EXH: B.F.A.C., *Some Neglected English Masters*, 1932, No. 85; Arts Council, *English Conversation Pieces of the 18th Century*, 1946, No. 24.

In the centre a small boy in a grown-up's feathered hat and red coat looks down towards a little girl on the left arranging his coat; a baby girl wearing a large bonnet sits on the ground in front, right.

It has been suggested (cf. Upton catalogue) that these are the three children of Philip Reinagle: Ramsay Richard and his sisters Charlotte and Fanny. If this is so the date of the picture must be c. 1780, for the child in the centre, who is probably a boy, is aged about five (Ramsay Richard was born in 1775). All three children followed their father's profession. Charlotte exhibited at the Academy from 1798–1808 and Fanny from 1799–1820. Their brother, elected R.A. in 1823, was like his father a painter of animals and landscape.

60 POND, ARTHUR (?)
See *English* (c. 1745)

63 SIR HENRY RAEBURN, R.A., 1756–1823

The Macdonald Children (*Plate Ib*)

Canvas, 56½ × 44¾ in.

INSCRIBED: (left), *Sir Henry Raeburn, R.S.A., pinxt;* and (right), *Ranald Macdonald of Clanranald and two younger brothers.*

COLL: F. E. Hills in 1895; his sale, Christie's, 2 July 1920, lot 39, repd.: bt. by Davis; acquired by Lord Bearsted by 1929.

LIT: Sir Walter Armstrong, *Sir Henry Raeburn*, London, 1901, p. 107, Pl. XXVII; J. L. Caw, *Portraits of Raeburn*, Edinburgh, 1909, repd.; J. Greig, *Sir Henry Raeburn*, London, 1911, p. 51, repd. p. XX.

EXH: R.A., Winter, 1895, No. 17; Guildhall, London, 1899, No. 174; Musée Moderne, Brussels, *Pictures by Turner and his Contemporaries*, 1929, No. 127; R.A., Winter, *British Art*, 1934, No. 197 (*Commemorative Catalogue*, No. 282, Pl. LXXXIII); R.A., Winter, *Scottish Art*, 1939, No. 97; R.A., Winter, *European Masters of the 18th Century*, 1954, No. 401; Whitechapel, 1955, No. 17; Arts Council, National Gallery, Edinburgh, *Raeburn Bicentenary*, 1956, No. 18.

ENGRAVED: by Arthur Hogg, 1921 (mezzotint).

The eldest of the Macdonald children, Reginald George, sits on a rock with his brother Robert, each with an arm about the other's waist, in the act of snapping their fingers over their heads, the former dressed in scarlet with white collar and stockings, the latter wearing a lemon-coloured dress, wide blue sash and white collar; the youngest boy, Donald, stands by their side, wearing scarlet and caressing a dog. The weakness of the composition is emphasized by J. Pope-Hennessy (*Burlington Magazine*, LXXIV, 1939, p. 68) in an article on the exhibition of *Scottish Art* at the Academy.

Reginald George Macdonald of Clanranald (1788–1873), succeeded as 19th Chief of Clanranald and 7th of Benbecula at the age of five. He represented Plympton in Parliament from 1812 to 1824. Later, financial difficulties forced him to sell his estates. The title fell to his son, Admiral Sir Reginald George Macdonald, by his first marriage with Caroline, daughter of the 2nd Earl of Mount Edgcumbe, by whom he also had four daughters. His second and third marriages were without issue. Of his two brothers, Robert died unmarried in 1864 and Donald, who entered the Civil Service, died unmarried in 1837.

Dated by Armstrong *c.* 1800.

64 SIR HENRY RAEBURN, R.A., 1756–1823

The 13th Earl of Eglinton as a Boy on Horseback

Canvas, 83½ × 59½ in.

COLL: Sir Charles Lamb (by marriage to Lady Mary Montgomerie, the mother of the boy depicted); thence by descent to Sir Archibald Lamb; his sale, Christie's, 28 April 1922, lot 48, repd.: bt. by Lord Bearsted.

EXH: see below (Related Picture).

RELATED PICTURE: a variant, in which the sitter is seen from closer to, is in the collection of the Earl of Eglinton. Mentioned in Armstrong, *Sir Henry Raeburn*, 1901, p. 101, and in Greig, *Sir Henry Raeburn*, 1911, p. 44, it is this picture according to Armstrong which was exhibited at the R.A., 1818, No. 32. The inferiority of the Eglinton version is remarked upon in the Upton catalogue, and this seems to be borne out by a comparison of the photographs. It may therefore be true that No. 64, although unnoticed in the literature, was the exhibited picture.

A small boy, he is seated astride a pony to left, and turns to face the spectator; he wears a yellow dress and dark cap; in the background is Eglinton Castle, which was rebuilt by the 12th Earl.

The succession of the 13th Earl is complicated. Archibald William Montgomerie (1812–61) was the son of Lord Montgomerie (who died in 1814, predeceasing his father the 12th Earl of Eglinton) and of Mary, daughter and eventual heiress of the 11th Earl of Eglinton (a kinsman of the 12th Earl); his mother married secondly, in 1815, Sir Charles Lamb, Bart. The boy succeeded to the title as 13th Earl on the death of his paternal grandfather in 1819, and was created 1st Earl de Winton in 1859. He married first Teresa Newcomen, by whom he had three sons and one daughter, and secondly Lady Adela Capel, daughter of the 6th Earl of Essex, by whom he had two daughters. He was a major-general; Lord Lieutenant of Ayrshire; Lord Lieutenant of Ireland in 1852 and 1858–59 and Knight of the Thistle, 1853. It was he who held the celebrated tournament at Eglinton Castle in 1839 (cf., e.g., Disraeli,

Plate Ia Romney (68)

Plate Ib Raeburn (63)

Plate Ic Hardy (67)

Plate Id Hogarth (43)

Plate IIa Stubbs (84)

Plate IIb Marshall (50)

Plate IIc Dance (13)

Plate IId Devis (17)

Endymion, vol. II, ch. 23). The same sitter is depicted when grown-up by Laporte in No. 47.

66 SIR JOSHUA REYNOLDS, P.R.A., 1723–1792

The Earl and Countess of Ely

Canvas, $95 \times 71\frac{1}{2}$ in.

INSCRIBED: *Henry Earl of Ely Anne Countess of Ely 1775*

COLL: by family descent; Marquess of Ely sale, Christie's, 25 July 1891, lot 72: bt. by Lesser; sold by Lesser to Jules Porge sometime after 1892; Alexandre Zygomalas sale, Christie's, 2 July 1920, lot 44, repd: bt. by Davis. Date of acquisition by Lord Bearsted unrecorded.

LIT: Graves and Cronin, *Reynolds*, London, 1899–1901, vol. I, pp. 288–9 (with incorrect measurements); Sir W. Armstrong, *Reynolds*, London, 1900, p. 204 (measurements as above); E. K. Waterhouse, *Reynolds*, London, 1941, p. 66, Pl. 170.

EXH: Dublin, 1873, No. 272; R.A., Winter, 1892, No. 109; Whitechapel, 1955, No. 7.

Full length, walking to the right before a pair of columns surmounting a plinth decorated with a relief; he wears a grey coat and waistcoat embroidered with silver braid, white stock and hose; his wife, who holds his right arm, is wearing a pink dress with white scarf and lace frills, her hair piled high and adorned with red, white and blue ostrich feathers.

Henry Loftus (1709–83) succeeded his nephew as 4th Viscount Loftus in 1769, the Earldom of Ely having expired with the latter's death. In 1771 he was created Earl of Ely. At his death the honours again expired but the estates devolved upon his nephew who was later to become Earl and then Marquess of Ely. He is depicted with his second wife, Anne, whom he married in 1775. She was the daughter of Capt. Hugh Bonfoy, R.N. and Anne Eliot (whom Reynolds painted in 1753–54) and became Lady of the Bedchamber to the Princesses. A portrait by Angelica Kauffmann showing the Earl with his first wife Frances Munroe, dated 1771, is in the National Gallery of Ireland.

There seems no reason, as in the Upton catalogue, to doubt the date of 1775 inscribed on the picture (which is accepted by Waterhouse) and the Earl's marriage in that year to Anne Bonfoy would provide an occasion for this double portrait. The date of 1781, which instead is given, is the year in which, according

to Graves and Cronin, Reynolds's account for £115 was settled (20 July). No sitters' book is preserved for 1775.

67 ROMNEY

See *Hardy, Thomas*

68 GEORGE ROMNEY, 1734–1802

William Beckford (*Plate Ia*)

Canvas, 93×57 in.

COLL: by descent from William Beckford's younger daughter Susannah, who married Alexander, 10th Duke of Hamilton; thence Hamilton Palace until sold at Christie's, 6 November 1919, lot 55, repd., as Alderman Beckford: bt. by Davis. Date of acquisition by Lord Bearsted unrecorded.

LIT: H. Ward and W. Roberts, *Romney*, London, 1904, p. 9; L. Melville, *Life and Letters of William Beckford*, London, 1910, p. 174, repd.; Avray Tipping, 'Hamilton Palace Collection of Pictures', *Country Life*, XLVI, 1919, pp. 515–16, Pl. 2; G. Chapman, *A Bibliography of William Beckford of Fonthill*, London, 1930, pp. 116–17; idem, *Beckford*, London, 1937, p. 87.

EXH: Edinburgh, 1883, No. 16; Edinburgh, *Loan Exhibition of Old Masters and Scottish National Portraits*, 1886, No. 1470; Glasgow, *International Exhibition*, 1888, No. 128; Whitechapel, 1955, No. 13 (Pl. II in catalogue).

He stands full length, looking to the right, leaning with his right arm on a sculptured pedestal. He wears a plum-coloured coat with white waistcoat and stock, buff-coloured breeches and white hose; behind, to the left, a building with acanthus pattern frieze and right, deer among trees.

Considerable confusion exists between portraits of Beckford and his father, Alderman Beckford, and also those of William Courtenay which William Beckford commissioned and owned. It is however certain that the present picture (which was catalogued in the Hamilton Palace sale and by Ward and Roberts as Alderman Beckford) is the portrait of the younger William Beckford mentioned in Romney's *Diary* of 1781–82, no doubt painted to commemorate his coming of age in 1781.

William Beckford (1760–1844), was the son of William Beckford, Alderman and Lord Mayor of London, who died in 1770. His chief monument, Fonthill Abbey, was begun in 1796 under James Wyatt and by the end of 1800 was sufficiently far advanced for a fête in Nelson's honour to be held there. The creator of this Gothic extravaganza, who is seen here in one of Romney's most classical and grand compositions, sold the Abbey and many of its contents in 1822, moving to Bath where he lived until his death. His publications include *Vathek* and letters written on his travels in Europe. He married Lady Margaret Gordon, daughter of the 4th Earl of Aboyne, by whom he had two daughters.

69 FRANCIS SARTORIUS, 1734–1804

A Man on Horseback

Canvas, 13¾ × 17½ in.

SIGNED: *F. Sartorius. pinxit*

COLL: previous history and date of acquisition by Lord Bearsted unrecorded.

EXH: Whitechapel, *English Sporting Pictures*, 1950, No. 71.

He rides to the left in an open landscape, wearing a blue coat, his head turned to the spectator, accompanied by two whippets; on the right is a small house on a slight rise.

70 FRANCIS SARTORIUS, 1734–1804

Peter Beckford's Hounds

Canvas, 38¼ × 47¾ in.

COLL: Peter Beckford, Stepleton House (whose son succeeded his uncle as Lord Rivers and assumed the name of Pitt); thence by family descent to the Hon. Gertrude Pitt; her sale, Christie's, 30 May 1919, lot 133: bt. by Amor; acquired by Lord Bearsted by 1928.

LIT: A. H. Higginson, *Peter Beckford Esq.*, London, 1937, pp. 23, 273, repd.

EXH: Knoedler, London, *Old Sporting Pictures*, 1928, No. 11; Whitechapel, 1955, No. 14.

RELATED PICTURES: two paintings by Sartorius, each showing two couples of Beckford's hounds, are Nos. 71 and 72 in the collection.

A park, with a view of Stepleton House (Iwerne Minster, Dorset) in the distance; in the foreground Beckford's pack of hounds with two hunt servants, who wear a livery of buff coats with black facings; they carry short swords, a privilege merited by their master being a ranger of Cranborne Chase.

Peter Beckford (1740–1811), a cousin of William Beckford of Fonthill, married in 1783 Louisa, daughter of Lord Rivers, his son becoming the 3rd Lord Rivers by special patent. He was the first English writer to describe the science of hunting and he is perhaps best known for his *Thoughts on Hunting*, published in 1781.

Probably painted at about the same time as Nos. 71 and 72, i.e. 1785, two years before Beckford relinquished his pack on setting out for Italy. Several of the hounds whose portraits appear in Nos. 71 and 72 are incorporated in the present picture; the one being sick in the foreground, for example, is Belmaid and corresponds exactly to the portrait in No. 72. Other hounds which can be recognized are Guider, who leads the pack, and Mannerley (both from No. 72).

71 FRANCIS SARTORIUS, 1734–1804

Two Couples of Foxhounds in a Park Landscape with two Terriers

Canvas, 29⅛ × 35⅛ in.

SIGNED AND DATED: *Frs. Sartorius. Pinxt. 1785*

INSCRIBED: with names and pedigrees of the four hounds in panel below, *Crazy, Blameless, Brilliant, Pillager*.

COLL: as No. 70; Hon. Gertrude Pitt sale, Christie's, 30 May 1919, lot 134, with companion: bt. by Knoedler; date of acquisition by Lord Bearsted unrecorded.

LIT: A. H. Higginson, *Peter Beckford Esq.*, London, 1937, pp. 99–105, repd.

COMPANION PICTURE: No. 72.

The hounds in the present picture belong to Peter Beckford's pack, shown in No. 70; cf. also No. 72.

72 FRANCIS SARTORIUS, 1734–1804

Two Couples of Hounds in a Park Landscape with two Terriers

Canvas, 29¼ × 35⅛ in.

SIGNED AND DATED: *Frs. Sartorius Pinxt. 1785*

INSCRIBED: with names and pedigrees of the four hounds in panel below, *Belman, Mannerly, Belmaid, Guider*.

COLL: as No. 71.

LIT: as No. 71.

COMPANION PICTURE: No. 71.

See No. 71. Belmaid, Mannerly and Guider are exactly repeated in Sartorius's painting of the pack (No. 70).

77 ROBERT SMIRKE, R.A., 1752–1845

A Scene from 'The Busybody'

Canvas, 20 × 20 in. (painted area circular, diam. 18¾ in.).

COLL: J. Haywood Hawkins in 1868; anonymous sale, Christie's, 1 June 1928, lot 91: bt. by Miller; acquired by Lord Bearsted by 1932.

EXH: Leeds, 1868, No. 1143; B.F.A.C., 1932, No. 37.

The episode illustrated is Act IV, Scene II, when Isabinda pretends to swoon in order to prevent her father, Sir Jealous Traffick, from getting at the cupboard in which her lover is concealed. Patch, her servant, is kneeling beside her mistress with a feigned show of concern for her condition. Isabinda wears a white blouse and yellow skirt, Patch an orange skirt and Sir Jealous Traffick a blue coat and red waistcoat with gold frogging.

The Busybody, a comedy by Mrs. Centlivre (born Susanna Carroll), an actress and dramatist who married Queen Anne's chef, was first produced in 1709.

78 ROBERT SMIRKE, R.A., 1752–1845

A Scene from 'Taste'

Canvas on panel, 12¾ × 8⅝ in.

COLL: Sir Hugo de Bathe sale, Sotheby's, 13 May 1931, lot 54: bt. by Wilson; Sir Kenneth Clark; date of acquisition by Lord Bearsted unrecorded.

EXH: Whitechapel, 1955, No. 16.

RELATED PICTURE: a similar picture from the collection of Sir George Beaumont was sold at Sotheby's, 30 June 1948, lot 44 (and see below).

A fat elderly woman ('Lady Pentweazle') is seated in an armchair, facing the spectator, hands folded on her lap, wearing a white satin dress and a blue bow and ostrich feathers in her hair.

The same lady forms half of a similar composition entitled *Conquest*, formerly in the collection of the late W. King (exhibited

R.A., 1796, No. 94 and engraved by David Lucas: repd. in *Art Quarterly*, XVII, 1954, p. 250 illustrating an article by A. Jaffé entitled 'John Smart, Miniature Painter: His Life and Iconography'). In that picture, which represents a scene from Act 1 of the farce *Taste* by Samuel Foote (1752), Lady Pentweazle is the object of admiration of the artist, Mr. Carmine, who forms the right-hand side of the composition. According to Mr. Jaffé, Smart may have posed for this figure.

82 STUBBS

See *Zoffany (Attributed to)*

83 GEORGE STUBBS, A.R.A., 1724–1806

The Haymakers

Panel ((?) Enamel colours, on oak), 36 × 54 in.

SIGNED AND DATED: *Geo: Stubbs pinxit 1783*

COLL: Sir Walter Gilbey by 1898; his sale, Christie's, 11 June 1915, lot 387: bt. by Agnew; with Knoedler, 1919, from whom acquired by Lord Bearsted.

LIT: Sir Walter Gilbey, *Life of George Stubbs*, London, 1898, p. 148, No. 6; E. R. Dibdin, 'Liverpool Art and Artists in the 18th Century', *Walpole Society*, VI, 1918, p. 64 (note), Pl. XXI; W. S. Sparrow, *British Sporting Artists*, London, 1922, p. 129, repd.; W. S. Sparrow, *George Stubbs and Ben Marshall*, London, 1929, p. 34, repd.; S. Sitwell, *Narrative Pictures*, London, 1937, pp. 53, 108, Pl. 73.

EXH: (?) R.A., 1786, No. 94; Walker Art Gallery, Liverpool, *Historical Exhibition of Liverpool Art*, 1908, No. 164; Stedelijk Museum, Amsterdam, *Twee Eeuwen Engelsche Kunst*, 1936, No. 154; Whitechapel, 1955, No. 9 (Pl. V in catalogue).

ENGRAVED: by Stubbs, 1791 (mezzotint). This shows a variation of the present composition, and is identical with the picture mentioned below (Related Pictures, I).

RELATED PICTURES: (I) A painting lent anonymously to the *Stubbs Exhibition*, Whitechapel Art Gallery, 1957, No. 45, shows a variation of the group with three additional figures. In the exhibition catalogue this picture is cited as the one exhibited at the Academy in 1786, although Gilbey and subsequent writers refer to the Upton picture as being the one shown in that exhibition. The anonymously owned picture is the same size as the present one, on panel, signed and dated 1785. The engraving (see above) follows this picture. (II) A variant, in the shape of an oval Wedgwood plaque, signed and dated 1795, is in the Lady Lever Gallery, Port Sunlight.

COMPANION PICTURE: No. 84.

A landscape with a group of haymakers at work in the late afternoon. Two women stand by a haywain, one holding a rake, the other turning over hay; a man forks it up to his companion, who reaches over to lift it on to the loaded cart, to which a pair of horses is harnessed; a clump of trees right, and a view over an extensive landscape.

Like many other paintings by Stubbs, the three in the Bearsted collection are badly abraded. This may be due to the fact that Stubbs was here using enamel colours and not oil paint. In his introduction to the exhibition of Stubbs's work held at the Whitechapel Art Gallery in 1957, Basil Taylor writes (p. 10): 'The change which takes place in his methods about 1770 can be attributed largely to his use of enamel colours; these are similar in consistency to gouache and demand a similar fluidity of application, essentially a watercolour technique in fact. After 1770 we find a frequent use of panels which offered the same untextured ground as the smoother surface of the white flux of the Wedgwood tablet.'

The Wedgwood plaques must have been fired and can be washed without harm, but if it is correct to infer that Stubbs was in the habit of using enamel colours on canvas or panel after c. 1770, it would explain the damage that might have resulted through cleaning to much of his later work, and in this instance to the three pictures at Upton.

84 GEORGE STUBBS, A.R.A., 1724–1806

The Reapers (*Plate IIa*)

Panel ((?)Enamel colours on oak), 36 × 54 in.

SIGNED AND DATED: *Geo: Stubbs pinxit 1783*

COLL: Sir Walter Gilbey by 1898; his sale, Christie's, 11 June 1915, lot 388: bt. by Agnew; with Knoedler, 1919, from whom acquired by Lord Bearsted.

LIT: Sir Walter Gilbey, *Life of George Stubbs*, London, 1898, p. 148, No. 7; E. R. Dibdin, 'Liverpool Art and Artists in the 18th Century', *Walpole Society*, VI, 1918, p. 64 (note), Pl. XXIb; W. S. Sparrow, *British Sporting*

Artists, London, 1922, p. 124, repd.; R. H. Wilenski, *English Painting*, London, 1933, Pl. 52a; anon article, 'At the Royal Academy', *Connoisseur*, XCIII, 1934, p. 115, repd.; S. Sitwell, *Narrative Pictures*, London, 1937, Pl. 72; W. Gaunt, *British Painting from Hogarth's Day to Ours*, London, 1945, Pl. 6; E. K. Waterhouse, *Painting in Britain*, London, 1953, p. 219, Pl. 179b.

EXH: (?)R.A., 1786, No. 77; Walker Art Gallery, Liverpool, *Historical Exhibition of Liverpool Art*, 1908, No. 190; Knoedler, London, *Old Sporting Pictures*, 1928, No. 6; R.A., Winter, *British Art*, 1934, No. 411 (*Commemorative Catalogue*, No. 171, Pl. LXVII); Stedelijk Museum, Amsterdam, *Twee Eeuwen Engelsche Kunst*, 1936, No. 155.

ENGRAVED: by Stubbs, 1791 (mezzotint). This shows a variation of the present composition, and is identical to the picture mentioned below (Related Pictures, I).

RELATED PICTURES: (I) A painting lent anonymously to the *Stubbs Exhibition*, Whitechapel Art Gallery, 1957, No. 44, shows a variation of the group with two additional figures. In the exhibition catalogue this picture is cited as the one exhibited at the Academy in 1786, although Gilbey and subsequent writers refer to the Upton picture as being the one shown in that exhibition. The anonymously owned picture is the same size as the present one, on panel, signed and dated 1784. The engraving (see above) follows this picture. (II) An oval Wedgwood plaque, signed and dated 1795, formerly in the collection of Major Malcolm and sold at Sotheby's, 18 November 1959, lot 43, shows another variation.

COMPANION PICTURE: No. 83.

A landscape with elm trees, left, and a cornfield where a farmer mounted on a bay cob stops to converse with the reapers; a girl stands facing the spectator, twisting two wisps of wheat ready to bind a sheaf which a man is holding; another man cuts the corn with a sickle, while a third stacks the sheaves, left.

For a note on the medium of this picture, cf. No. 83.

85 GEORGE STUBBS, A.R.A., 1724–1806

The Labourers

Panel ((?)Enamel colours on oak), 36 × 54 in.

SIGNED AND DATED: *Geo: Stubbs p; 1779*

COLL: Sir Walter Gilbey by 1898; his sale, Christie's, 11 June 1915, lot 386: bt. by Agnew; with Knoedler, 1919, from whom acquired by Lord Bearsted.

LIT: Joseph Mayer, *Memoirs of Thomas Dodd, William Upcott and George Stubbs*, Liverpool, 1879, p. 29; Sir Walter Gilbey, *Life of George Stubbs*, London, 1898, pp. 155–6, No. 16.

EXH: R.A., 1779, No. 322.

ENGRAVED: the group of figures and horse and cart, by Stubbs, 1789 (mezzotint).

RELATED PICTURES: a picture dated 1767 with the central group of the bricklayers and horse and cart, but in a different landscape of a rustic type reputedly added by Amos Green, is in the Museum of Art, Philadelphia (McFadden Coll.): cf. Gilbey, *op. cit.*, p. 175. A mezzotint of this subject by Richard Earlom is reproduced in W. S. Sparrow, *George Stubbs and Ben Marshall*, London, 1929, pp. 30–31. The picture was also engraved by Henry Birche in 1790.

Mayer mentions, among several versions, a Wedgwood plaque in the collection of Thomas West, and another, 'the largest plate of earthenware ever made', then in the collection of Erasmus Darwin.

A park landscape with, left, four labourers arguing over the tailboard of a horse and cart from which they have just unloaded bricks, near the edge of a wood; one leans on a stick, another lifts the tailboard of the cart, a third stands by doing nothing, while the fourth is about to get up from a sitting position in the cart. In the background is an entrance lodge to a park; at the right a dog is lying in front of a group of four trees.

Mayer recounts how the *Bricklayers* was painted by Stubbs in 1778 at Southill, which then belonged to Viscount Torrington, for whom Stubbs did 'a great deal of work. The idea (for the picture) was Lord Torrington's. He had often watched his men at work and thought what a telling picture might be made of them in the Flemish style. The horse represented was a favourite old hunter . . .' Mayer goes on to say how Stubbs had the workmen loading and unloading the cart, and when at length they started quarrelling over the manner of fixing the tailpiece, the artist saw his opportunity for the painting. The existence of a similar picture, painted twelve years before, casts some doubt upon this story, nor does the appearance or treatment of the horse suggest that it was a favourite old hunter.

The Southill estate was bought by William Whitbread in 1795 and shortly afterwards James Holland was commissioned to remodel the house. The lodge shown in the present picture, if it was ever built at Southill, is no longer in existence. It is however possible that it was one designed by Isaac Ware, who was probably working at Southill in c. 1745, which has since been destroyed.

For a note on the medium of the present picture, cf. No. 73.

90 WILLIAM TURNER of Oxford, 1789–1862

Lincoln Horse Fair

Canvas, $14\frac{1}{2} \times 24\frac{3}{4}$ in.

SIGNED AND DATED: *W. H. Turner 1858*

COLL: G. Clothier sale, Christie's, 29 November 1890, lot 90: bt. by Volkins; Sir Walter Gilbey sale, Christie's, 15 March 1910, lot 159: bt. by Cusnick; acquired by Lord Bearsted by 1937.

EXH: 39 Grosvenor Square, London, *British Country Life through the Centuries*, 1937, No. 258.

A flat landscape with a large assembly of horses and figures.

91 THOMAS WEAVER, 1774–1843

John Corbet and the Warwickshire Foxhounds

Canvas, $27\frac{3}{8} \times 35\frac{1}{2}$ in.

SIGNED AND DATED: *T. Weaver pinxt. 1812*

COLL: Lord Middleton (who may have commissioned the picture and according to the Upton catalogue sold it to Col. Birkin); the latter's sale, Christie's, 7 December 1934, lot 70: bt. by Halliday; date of acquisition by Lord Bearsted unrecorded.

LIT: W. S. Sparrow, *Book of Sporting Pictures*, London, 1931, p. 86, repd.; *idem*, 'Thomas Weaver of Shropshire', *Connoisseur*, XCIV, 1934, p. 388.

EXH: Leamington Spa Art Gallery, *Art Treasurers of Warwickshire*, 1948, No. 9.

ENGRAVED: by Richard Woodman, 1828.

RELATED PICTURES: in a letter to the Leamington Spa *Courier* in 1896, St. John Corbet, son of the M.F.H., remarks that the original picture had passed into the collection of Mr. Harold Weaver, grandson of the artist, having been 'sold some years before at Severn Hill and bought by a chemist named Pyefinch' —cf. Sir Charles Mordaunt and W. R. Verney, *Annals of the Warwickshire Hunt 1795–1895*, London, 1896, vol. II, p. 303. He adds that a companion picture was 'at Shrewsbury'.

He is seen in the centre foreground of a landscape, mounted on a grey horse, waving on hounds; left, behind him, the huntsman Will Barrow and a hunt servant at a gate; in the distance members of the hunt can be seen.

John Corbet of Sundorne Castle took up the mastership of the Warwickshire in 1791 and hunted the country at his own expense. He was known as the 'Father of the Trojans', a reference to a famous hound in his pack (said to be represented as the leading hound in the picture). In 1811 he was succeeded in the mastership by the 6th Lord Middleton who paid 1,200 guineas for the pack. He died in 1817.

The fact that the picture is dated 1812 and was in the collection of Lord Middleton (who took over the pack in 1811) may imply that it was commissioned as a portrait to commemorate Corbet's association with the Warwickshire hounds.

The 'original' version referred to in the Leamington Spa *Courier* as having been owned by the chemist Pyefinch may have had a similar origin, but it is equally possible that it was painted at an earlier period during Corbet's mastership. The name of Pyefinch has perhaps some significance in this context, for Weaver married Susannah Pyefinch, the daughter of the Rev. John Pyefinch of Westbury, Shropshire, and was the father of the painter John Pyefinch Weaver.

92 ROBERT WEST, d. 1770

Thomas Smith and his Family

Canvas, $23\frac{3}{8} \times 35\frac{1}{8}$ in.

SIGNED AND DATED: *R. West fecit. 1735*

COLL: a typed sheet of paper attached to the back of the canvas gives the information that the picture descended in the family of Thomas Smith's eldest son, John Smith of Evesham. It is not known when it first came to Upton.

EXH: Arts Council, *English Conversation Pieces of the 18th Century*, 1946, No. 10; Leamington Spa Art Gallery, *Art Treasures of Warwickshire*, 1948, No. 10.

A panelled room with Thomas Smith seated left before a fireplace with his three sons round him; his wife stands at his left, wearing an embroidered dress, next to her is her eldest daughter holding a baby and, at the right, at a circular tripod table are three girls, the eldest of whom is pouring out tea; a black servant stands at the extreme right with a kettle on a tripod stand.

Some biographical details are given on the sheet of paper referred to above. The head of the family, Thomas Smith (1672–1739)—according to the Upton catalogue his original name was Le Fevre and he was of French extraction—married Anne Horne. It is not clear whether the boy at the extreme left is the eldest son John or the second son Thomas (1726–88); the boy with the dog is the third son, Culling (d. 1781), whose son married Lady Anne Mornington, the Duke of Wellington's sister; the baby in arms is William (1735–1819), who married Sarah Sumner, sister of Humphrey Sumner, Provost of King's and headmaster of Eton. He is held by the eldest daughter, Anne; the second daughter Charlotte (who married John Munro) is pouring out tea, and the two small girls at either side of the table are Maria (married a Burrows) and Frances (married a Cottrell).

The artist is probably the Robert West about whom little more is known than that he studied in Paris under van Loo, and in 1744 or earlier established a drawing school in Dublin. W. G. Strickland, *Dictionary of Irish Artists*, Dublin, 1913, adds that 'he does not appear to have used the brush', a statement which is contradicted if the present picture is from his hand. In the catalogue of the Arts Council exhibition the picture is described as being primitive in character and therefore probably an early work. Robert West was the father of Francis Robert West who succeeded him as master in the Dublin Society School.

98 RICHARD WILSON, R.A., 1714–1782

A Convent on a Rock

Canvas, $14 \times 17\frac{1}{2}$ in.

COLL: previous history and date of acquisition by Lord Bearsted unrecorded.

LIT: W. G. Constable, *Richard Wilson*, London, 1953, p. 198, Pl. 76a.

RELATED PICTURES: Constable lists five versions, differing in minor details but all, unlike

No. 98, with a tower beyond the bridge at the left. These are: (1) Stanley Marling coll.; (2) Lady Holmes sale, Sotheby's, 20 February 1952, lot 85: bt. by Manetti; Exh., Tate Gallery, *Wilson*, 1955, No. 53; (3) Col. R. H. Brocklebank coll.; (4) R. B. Beckett coll.; (5) with Katz, London, 1950.

At the right a Renaissance building surmounts a classical structure which has been built on a rock or artificial rampart; two figures are resting in front; the ground falls away to a river and bridge at the left.

Constable, who catalogues the Upton version as the original, gives details of the history of the composition, which has been variously entitled *A View in Italy* (as in the Upton catalogue), *Santa Maria Aventina*, *Sant' Anselmo on the Aventine*, and *Convento della Vittoria*. The latter three are not reconcilable with the subject and a more apposite title may be provided by an entry in Faringdon's *Diary* (unpublished) for 2 October 1803: 'West (i.e. Benjamin West) has been cleaning his collection of pictures . . . . He dwelt upon his little picture (its size was given as 13 × 16 in. in West's sale) of the Convent on the Rock by Wilson saying it was coloured equal to Cuyp or Both & in parts equal to Titian.' This is perhaps the picture which later entered the collection of Samuel Rogers and was included in his sale in 1856. (Nos. 3 and 5 in the versions listed above have been claimed to be this work, which was exhibited at the B.I. in 1817.) There is also the possibility that No. 98 is the painting in question although there is no indication on the back of the Christie stencils that it might have been expected to acquire in its passage through that sale room (West and Samuel Rogers sales).

103 JOHN WOOTTON, c. 1686–1765

A Classical Landscape with Animals

Canvas, $44\frac{1}{2} \times 42\frac{1}{2}$ in.

COLL: previous history and date of acquisition by Lord Bearsted unrecorded.

A sunset landscape, with a herdsman driving horses, sheep and cattle to water in a lake surrounded by wooded banks; at the extreme left can be seen part of a classical temple.

Wootton, usually associated with equestrian portraits, etc., in landscapes, also produced classical landscapes such as No. 103 throughout his life (cf. M. H. Grant, *Old English Landscape Painters*, 1926, vol. I, pp. 25–26). It is uncertain whether he ever visited Rome, but he was greatly influenced by Gaspard Poussin, as was noted by Vertue in 1722 (cf. *Vertue Notebooks*, I, p. 101, *Walpole Society*, XVIII), and the sale of his studio in 1761 included eleven copies after Gaspard. The well-observed animals in the present picture are somewhat anomalous in this classical scene.

82 Attributed to JOHANN ZOFFANY, R.A., 1734/5–1810

A Man with a Gun

Canvas, $27\frac{1}{4} \times 35\frac{1}{2}$ in.

COLL: C. Wilson sale, Christie's, 16 May 1913, lot 35, as Early English School: bt. by Knoedler; with Agnew, 1923, from whom acquired by Lord Bearsted.

LIT: W. S. Sparrow, *British Sporting Artists*, London, 1922, p. 133, repd.

EXH: Whitechapel, *Five Centuries of European Painting*, 1948, No. 56; Whitechapel, 1955, No. 8 (Pl. IV in catalogue).

A young man stands in a landscape, left, wearing a dark-green coat with white waistcoat and breeches and black hat, drawing the cleaning rod from his gun; a pointer and dead partridge at his feet; a groom with two horses appearing over the brow of a hill at the right.

Formerly catalogued as a portrait of 'Mr. Poyntz of Bath' by Stubbs. This attribution is unconvincing and the style is much nearer to that of Zoffany. The identification of the sitter goes back to the Christie sale of 1913 and may have some substance, but it is possible that it was based on a misconception arising from a superficial resemblance to William Poyntz (son of Stephen Poyntz of Midgham, Berkshire) in the 1762 (Bath) portrait by Gainsborough which is at Althorp. On the evidence of dress No. 82 is dated by Mrs. Harris in the early 1770's.

The Dutch School

111 JAN VAN DER CAPPELLE,
c. 1623/5–1679

A River Estuary (*Plate IVd*)

Canvas, $28\frac{1}{2} \times 41\frac{1}{2}$ in.

COLL: H. A. J. Munro in 1835; his sale, Christie's, 1 June 1861, lot 88: bt. by Tayleur; J. Tayleur sale, Christie's, 13 April 1923, lot 43, repd.: bt. by Colnaghi; with Knoedler, from whom acquired by Lord Bearsted.

LIT: Waagen, vol. II, p. 140 (Munro); H. de Groot, 1923, vol. VII, No. 106.

EXH: B.I., 1835, No. 138.

A wide waterway with a view out to sea, seen beneath a grey sky; on the right a small vessel before the wind, laden with passengers, and nearby a fishing boat with two figures; on the left a States Yacht with a boat pulling away and various small craft sheltered by a spit of land; a church and buildings seen beyond.

112 Style of JACOB GERRITSZ CUYP,
1594–1651/2

Anna Maria Mockels as a Child

Panel (Oak), $45\frac{1}{2} \times 33$ in.

INSCRIBED: *Anna Maria Siedonia Mockels . . . geborgen Anno . . . und gestorben Anno 1650 . . .*

COLL: Hon. W. Lowther sale, Christie's, 10 May 1912, lot 9, as by J. G. Cuyp: bt. by Davis with its pair; date of acquisition by Lord Bearsted not recorded. A label on the back states that the picture, painted by Albert Cuyp, was 'bought April 1894 of Mr. Cahn belonged to Mr. Bruce'.

EXH: Whitechapel, 1955, No. 21.

COMPANION PICTURE: No. 113.

A small girl aged about six, standing full length to right in an architectural interior, is wearing a crimson frock trimmed with silver braid, white pinafore, white lace collar and cuffs, pearl necklace and gold chain to which is attached a medallion portrait; she holds a carnation in her left hand and a vase of flowers

stands on a settee by her side. Two coats of arms top left, the left hand being those of the family of Mockel of Westphalia.

Previously catalogued as by J. G. Cuyp. The flowers are by another hand. Prof. Gerson writes that he does not know the artist, but that in style it is not far removed from J. G. Cuyp.

113 Style of JACOB GERRITSZ CUYP,
1594–1651/2

A younger Brother of Anna Maria Mockels

Panel (Oak), $44\frac{3}{4} \times 32$ in.

COLL: as No. 112.

EXH: Whitechapel, 1955, No. 22 (Pl. IX in catalogue).

COMPANION PICTURE: No. 112.

A little boy, aged about three, standing full length to left in an architectural interior with a black and white paved floor, wearing a scarlet frock trimmed with silver braid, white lace collar and cuffs, white apron, scarlet cap with feathers and a double chain of coral beads; he holds a goldfinch on the index finger of his right hand, and a dog is seated beside him. Arms as in No. 112.

Previously catalogued as by J. G. Cuyp (cf. No. 112). The child appears to be a small boy, prior to being breeched, and not as hitherto supposed, a little girl.

114 MELCHIOR DE HONDECOETER,
1636–1695

A Turkey Cock and other Birds in a Garden

Canvas, $48\frac{1}{4} \times 64\frac{1}{4}$ in.

SIGNED AND DATED: *M d Hondecoeter Ao 1672*

COLL: first recorded by Waagen in the collection of Henry Labouchère, Lord Taunton; passed to his grandson E. A. V. Stanley and sold privately at the time of the Stanley sale, July 1920; with Buttery, 1920; with Knoedler, from whom acquired by Lord Bearsted.

LIT: Waagen, vol. II, p. 422 (Labouchère).

EXH: (?)Manchester Art Gallery, *Art Treasures*, 1857, No. 833.

A turkey cock, peacock and peahen, ducks and a chicken with chicks are seen near a river or pond on the far side of which is a small house; behind them, left, is part of a balustrade on which a cock and hen are perched.

Waagen mentions two large pictures of birds, 'the one . . . belonging in every respect . . . to his best productions. The other with a turkey cock is somewhat dark.' The present picture must be the second of these two. The first, which had belonged to Beckford, is now in the National Gallery of Australia, Melbourne. It is not clear which picture was exhibited in 1857.

115 DUTCH SCHOOL

See *Flinck*

116 After WILLEM CORNELISZ DUYSTER, *c.* 1599–1635

The Interior of a Barn with an Officer

Panel (Oak), $16\frac{1}{2} \times 12\frac{3}{4}$ in.

COLL: included in two anonymous sales at Christie's: 16 July 1937, lot 54, as by Pieter Codde: bt. by Roland; and 17 March 1939, lot 43, as by Duyster: bt. by Barnes. Date of acquisition by Lord Bearsted unrecorded.

EXH: Whitechapel, 1955, No. 25.

RELATED PICTURE: No. 116 is a copy of the autograph painting in the Mauritshuis.

A young officer, wearing a yellow doublet and green sash, stands in the centre facing left, his head turned towards the spectator; in the background a group of three soldiers are playing at dice on an upturned drum; above them is a hay-loft, and, right, some wooden steps.

The picture was previously catalogued as by Duyster, but it should rather be considered a copy of the superior version in the Mauritshuis.

115 GOVERT FLINCK, 1615–1660

A Child holding a Dog

Canvas, $36\frac{1}{8} \times 29$ in.

COLL: Earl of Ellenborough sale, Sotheby's, 11 June 1947, lot 39, as by A. Cuyp: bt. by

Leggatt, from whom acquired by Lord Bearsted the same year.

EXH: Whitechapel, 1955, No. 23 (Pl. X in catalogue).

A little girl aged about three is seated on a bank by a tree, facing the spectator; she wears a yellow coat and white apron over a white dress, lace cap, white cuffs and large white collar with red bows at her wrists and shoulders, and holds a small black and tan dog, with a red collar and bell, under her right arm; a landscape view, left.

The portrait appeared in the Upton catalogue as Dutch School, possibly of the 1640's, the name of Flinck being tentatively associated with it. In the Whitechapel exhibition it was catalogued without explanation as by J. G. Cuyp. Prof. Gerson writes that in the opinion of Dr. S. J. Gudlaugsson the picture is by Flinck, an attribution with which he concurs.

117 JAN VAN GOYEN, 1596–1656

A River Scene (*Plate IVc*)

Panel (Oak), $13\frac{1}{2} \times 24$ in.

SIGNED AND DATED: *V G 1643*

COLL: Sir George Drummond sale, Christie's, 26 June 1919, lot 179: bt. by Davis; date of acquisition by Lord Bearsted unrecorded.

LIT: H. de Groot, 1927, vol. VIII, No. 782.

A view looking along a river with peasants and cattle in a ferry-boat leaving the shore, left; on the bank are cottages, and a church spire seen above some trees; sailing boats in the distance and right, two men in a rowing boat with eel pots.

121 JOHANNES VAN HAENSBERGEN, 1642–1705

A Classical Landscape with Women bathing

Panel (Oak), $8\frac{5}{8} \times 10\frac{3}{4}$ in.

SIGNED: with Poelenbergh's initials (*C.P.*)

COLL: previous history and date of acquisition by Lord Bearsted unrecorded.

On the left a pool in which a group of women are bathing; two others converse over a pile of washing in the right foreground; a ruined building lies in a valley, beyond which are distant hills.

Formerly ascribed to Poelenbergh, but almost certainly by his pupil, Haensbergen. The positioning and accentuation of the signature are both suspicious, and the picture is clearly by the same hand as, for example, Haensbergen's *Women Bathing* in the Mauritshuis (No. 135).

118 JAN VAN DER HEYDEN, 1637–1712

Farm Buildings seen through an Archway (*Plate IIIb*)

Panel (Oak), $11\frac{1}{4} \times 10\frac{1}{4}$ in.

COLL: J. Kleinenbergh sale, Leiden, 19 July 1841, lot 65: bt. by de Gruyter; anonymous sale (Rev. J. Schuldham), Christie's, 28 June 1879, lot 103: bt. by Partington; C. T. D. Crews sale, Christie's, 1 July 1915, lot 33: bt. by Colnaghi; Henry Hirsh sale, Christie's, 12 June 1931, lot 5: bt. by Spink. Date of acquisition by Lord Bearsted unrecorded.

LIT: H. de Groot, 1927, vol. VIII, No. 252.

EXH: Whitechapel, 1955, No. 36 (Pl. XI in catalogue).

A track, on which are some sheep, leads under a ruined brick archway to a cottage and farm buildings; in the centre beyond the archway a shepherd sits by a fence with his dog.

Hofstede de Groot, cataloguing the picture under van der Heyden, attributes the figure and animals to Adriaen van der Velde. The sheep appear to be painted in the latter's style, and a disparity between them and the rest of the picture also suggests that they were added by another hand. Van der Velde, who is traditionally said to have added the figures to van der Heyden's paintings, died in 1672, and thereafter it is possible, as de Groot suggests, that the figures, still in the style of van der Velde, were painted by van der Heyden himself. In this undated example the collaboration of van der Velde is hypothetical.

HONDECOETER

See *De Hondecoeter* (No. 114)

HONTHORST

See *Van Honthorst* (No. 137)

119 JOHANNES JANSON, 1729–1784

A Winter Landscape

Panel (Oak), $11 \times 12\frac{3}{4}$ in.

SIGNED: *J. Janson f:*

COLL: previous history and date of acquisition by Lord Bearsted unrecorded.

A frozen river with figures skating; in the foreground on the right bank a man is cutting branches from a tree, while another gathers them; cottages on the left bank and a church in the distance.

120 GABRIEL METSU, 1629–1667

The Duet ('Le Corsage Bleu') (*Plate IIIc*)

Panel (Oak), $16 \times 11\frac{7}{8}$ in.

SIGNED: *G. Metsu*

COLL: the early history of this picture, before it appeared with its 'companion', *Corsage Rouge*, in the Randon de Boisset sale, is uncertain. Smith, but not de Groot, alleges that it was in the Tonneman sale, Amsterdam (18 October 1754) but Terwesten's description (*Catalogus . . . van Schilderyen*, 1770, p. 97) of lot 14 in this sale ('Een kabinet Stukje, zynde een Juffertje, dat op de viool de gambe speelt, met een Heer die zingt, teder en eel geschildert, door Gabriel Metsu, hoog 14 breit $11\frac{1}{2}$ duimen') is not applicable to No. 120. De Groot (No. 162d) lists a picture in the Witsen sale, Amsterdam, 25 May 1746, which he suggests may be either the present picture or his No. 155, the *Man and Woman with a Virginal*, now in the National Gallery. Hoet's (*Catalogus . . . van Schilderyen*, vol. II, 1752, p. 186) description of lot 4 (mistakenly for 5) in this sale ('Een Juffer met een satyne kleed aan, die met een Heer Musiceert teder en puyk door Gabriel Metsu; 1 voet $4\frac{1}{2}$ duim $\times$ 1 v 1 d') is not detailed enough to identify the picture with certainty but it may well refer to No. 120. It was bought by Quinkhard; Randon de Boisset sale, Paris, 27 February 1777, lot 81: bt. by de Morinières or Perrin (with companion); Destouches sale, Paris, 21 March 1794, lot 42: bt. by Le Brun (with companion); Wautier sale, Paris, 9 June 1797: bt. by Lafontain or Le Rouge (with companion); Robit sale, Paris, 21 May 1801, lot 70: bt. by Bryan (with companion). Bryan, who was furnished with credits by Mr. Hibbert and Sir Simon Clarke, acquired the present picture for the former, and the companion, *Corsage Rouge*, for the latter; Hibbert sale, Christie's, 13 June 1829, lot 65: no buyer recorded but lent by Joseph Neeld to 1831 exhibition; Sir John Neeld, 1878; Alfred de Rothschild (in this collection prior to Davis's catalogue of 1884); with Knoedler in 1924, from whom it was acquired by Lord Bearsted.

LIT: W. Buchanan, *Memoirs of Painting*, London, 1824, vol. II, p. 54, No. 70; and p. 56, No. 23, where Bryan's catalogue of the pictures bought at the Citoyen Robit sale is incorporated; Smith, 1833, vol. IV, No. 8; Waagen, vol. II, p. 246 (Neeld); C. Davis, *Catalogue of the Collection of Alfred de Rothschild*, London, 1884, vol. I, No. 19; Mrs. Erskine, 'Collection of Alfred de Rothschild', *Connoisseur*, III, 1902, p. 74; H. de Groot, 1907, vol. I, No. 149.

EXH: B.I., 1815, No. 74; B.I., 1851, No. 76; R.A., Winter, 1878, No. 119; Kleycamp Galleries, The Hague, *Oud-Hollandsche en Vlaamsche Meesters*, 1927, No. 29; Manchester Art Gallery, *Dutch Old Masters*, 1929, No. 37; R.A., Winter, *Dutch Art*, 1929, No. 234 (*Commemorative Catalogue*, p. 78); Slatter Galleries, London, *Masterpieces of Dutch Painting*, 1945, No. 13; Birmingham Art Gallery, *Some Dutch Cabinet Pictures of the 17th Century*, 1950, No. 40; Whitechapel, 1955, No. 34 (Pl. XXXVI in catalogue).

RELATED PICTURES: (1) A contemporary copy is in the collection of H.M. The Queen, Buckingham Palace (cf. L. Cust, *The Royal Collection of Paintings at Buckingham Palace*, London, 1905). (2) Smith gives the information that a picture of the same subject was sold with Mrs. Gordon's collection in 1808 for 75 gns. (i.e. 2 April, lot 95); (3) A larger picture (18½ × 16 in.) which has much in common with No. 120 is in the Rothschild Bequest, Waddesdon. It shows the same sitters, the woman wearing a similar dress, in a room with an identical chimney-piece (H. de Groot, No. 148).

RELATED DRAWING: a pencil study was in the collection of Lord Camden and was sold in the E. W. Lake sale at Christie's, 11 July 1845, lot 120 (not 6 May 1842 as stated by de Groot).

COMPANION PICTURE: *Le Corsage Rouge*, (H. de Groot, No. 97), although not strictly a pendant (its size is 13½ × 11 in. and it portrays one figure only) is described as such by Smith and, until separated at the Citoyen Robit sale, it accompanied No. 120. In 1842 (Smith, *Supplement*, No. 36) it belonged to Baron James de Rothschild, and was reunited for a time with *Le Corsage Bleu* in the Alfred de Rothildhsc collection (Mrs. Erskine, *op. cit.*).

A young lady wearing a blue jacket edged with ermine and a white satin skirt trimmed with gold braid sits at the right beside a table which is partly covered by a carpet; she holds a musical score on her lap and turns to look at a youth who sits on the farther side of the table tuning his guitar. A glass of wine stands between them, to the right is a large chimney-piece supported on columns, and in the foreground a King Charles spaniel.

122 EMANUEL MEURANT, 1622–1700

A Landscape with Cottages (*Plate IVa*)

Panel (Oak), 18¼ × 24½ in.

SIGNED AND DATED: *P. Potter f. . . 1646*

COLL: Sir George Phillips, 1882; Earl of Camperdown sale, Christie's, 21 February 1919, lot, 144: bt. by Simmons; anonymous sale, Christie's, 1 July 1921, lot 63: bt. by Mallet. Date of acquisition by Lord Bearsted unrecorded.

LIT: H. de Groot, 1912, vol. IV, No. 88 (as by Potter).

EXH: R.A., Winter, 1882, No. 69; Whitechapel, 1955, No. 28.

A cottage and Dutch barn at the left, bounded on two sides by a canal, with two cows in a pasture in front; a path and track, separated by a broken fence, lead past other cottages, right, into the distance; two men are walking along the track.

The attribution to Potter, accepted by de Groot, is questioned in the Upton catalogue, where the suggestion is made that the artist was probably Meurant. Prof. Gerson has written to say that he supports this attribution.

The signature is a tolerably good imitation of Potter's. There can however be no doubt that the attribution to Meurant is correct when the present painting is compared with a signed work (privately owned: exhibited Colnaghi's, 1961) which is extremely close in subject matter and in the almost monochrome treatment of colour and is clearly by the same hand as No. 122.

Meurant, whose dated works range from 1658–96, painted some pictures which are close to Potter in composition and execution (cf. H. Gerson, article in Thieme-Becker, *Künstler-Lexikon*, 1931, vol. XXV, p. 281).

121 POELENBERGH

See *Haensbergen*

122 POTTER(?)

See *Meurant*

123 Attributed to REMBRANDT VAN RIJN, 1606–1669

A Priest at an Altar

Panel (Oak), 22 × 19⅛ in.

SIGNED AND DATED: *Rembrandt f.* 16 . . (last two numerals indistinct).

COLL: according to de Groot (*infra*) the picture was in a sale at Amsterdam, 7 September 1803, lot 139 (i.e. Schmidt sale), and probably in the van Roothaan sale (Amsterdam, 29 March 1826, lot 52, as by Lievens). It was included in Miss Chippendall's sale, Christie's, 28 May 1903, lot 154: bt. by Nicholson; de Groot, who omits the Chippendall provenance, gives the ownership of T. Humphrey Ward and J. Walter of Bearwood; Arthur Walter sale, Christie's, 18 June 1937, lot 84, repd.: bt. by Barnes; date of acquisition by Lord Bearsted unrecorded.

LIT: H. de Groot, 'Nieuw Ontdekte Rembrandts (II)', *Onze Kunst*, XXII, 1912, p. 177; *idem*, 1916, vol. VI, No. 71; J. G. van Gelder, 'Rembrandt and his Circle', *Burlington Magazine*, XCV, 1953, p. 37.

EXH: R.A., Winter, *Dutch Pictures*, 1952, No. 38.

RELATED PICTURES: among a number of versions of this composition, all of which show the figure from a closer viewpoint than No. 123, are the following: (1) Prouvost sale, Brussels, 20 June 1928, lot 90; (2) Chiesa collection, Milan; (3) Pulaski collection, Paris; (4) Otto Buel, Lucerne, in 1935; (5) Jas sale, The Hague, 26 February 1941, lot 79; (6) Kasteel Wawel, Cracow (ex-Czosnowska), attributed to Lievens (cf. H. Schneider, *Jan Lievens*, Haarlem, 1932, p. 97, No. 22). This picture, which was exhibited as (?)Lievens in the Rembrandt Exhibition, Warsaw, 1956 (No. 52), has also been attributed to S. Koninck (cf. K. E. Simon, *Zeitschrift für Kunstgeschichte*, V, 1936, p. 143, note 5).

ENGRAVED: by Jean-Pierre Norblin (etching in reverse, 1781): this includes a mirror with a frame in the form of branches which is not visible in the picture.

The priest has the features of Rembrandt's father. He stands in profile to the left before an altar, wearing a golden robe and writing in a book which he supports on his left forearm; on the altar table, covered by a gold cloth, a large volume rests on part of a print which is suspended over the edge; in the background, right, a chair is placed beneath the heavy folds of a dark-green curtain; the scene is lit by two candles placed on the altar.

The present picture is regarded as the original by de Groot and by Schneider (in entry relating to the copy by Lievens), both dating it *c.* 1631–32. Van Gelder, who assumes that the original is lost and does not accept No. 123 as being by Rembrandt, gives a date of 1624–29. In a written communication, Prof. Gerson states that he is uncertain which of the versions is the original, or whether even the original is by Rembrandt.

The signature, hitherto unrecorded, does not appear to be authentic. The final indistinct numerals may be *28*. The balance of probabilities do not support a firm attribution to Rembrandt.

124 Follower of REMBRANDT VAN RIJN, 1606–1669

A Landscape with a Mill

Canvas, 32⅜ × 41¾ in.

COLL: Sir Simon Clarke and G. Hibbert sale, Christie's, 15 May 1802, lot 46, as by Rembrandt: buyer unrecorded but presumably bought in for it was included in Hibbert's sale, 13 June 1829, lot 22, as by Koninck: bt. by Emmerson; Emmerson sale, Phillips, 15 June 1832, lot 149, as by Rembrandt; Sir Samuel Scott, 1839 and 1861; Edward Scott, 1880; Sir Edward Scott sale, Christie's, 16 July 1943, lot 11, repd., as attributed to Rembrandt: bt. by Barnes; date of acquisition by Lord Bearsted unrecorded.

LIT: Smith, 1836, vol. VII, No. 605; H. de Groot, 1916, vol. VI, No. 967b; H. Gerson, *Koninck*, Berlin, 1936, p. 32, No. XXVI.

EXH: B.I., 1839, No. 16; B.I., 1861, No. 57; R.A., Winter, 1880, No. 82.

The mill stands among cottages at the right of a winding canal which broadens in the foreground; on the left is a bridge over a creek, which a rider on a white horse, accompanied by a running youth, has just crossed; a large building left, a church steeple beyond and various scattered figures.

Attributed in the past both to Rembrandt and Koninck. According to Gerson (*op. cit.*) it is not by the latter artist but is a later work influenced by Rembrandt. Gerson points out that the mill is copied from one of Rembrandt's etchings (cf. Münz, *Critical Catalogue*, 1952, vol. II, No. 145) and the running youth from the figure at the left of *The Night Watch*. A verbal attribution to Flinck, by H. M. Clark and Sir George Preston, is recorded in the Upton catalogue. The handling seems insufficiently individual for a precise attribution to be attempted.

No. 124 was previously entitled *Rembrandt's Father's Mill*, but the landscape is probably imaginary. The mill itself, shown in Rembrandt's dated etching of 1641, has not been identified, but for a review of the subject see J. G. van Gelder and N. F. van Gelder-Schrijver, 'De "Memorie" van Rembrandt's prenten in het bezit van Valerius Roever', *Oud Holland*, LV, 1938, pp. 8–10, and LVI, 1939, pp. 87–88, where the claims of Catwijk on the Rhine (a mill belonging to Rembrandt's family), Ossenbrugge and Suydbroeck bij Noordwijk are discussed.

An engraving of the mill at Katwijk op Ryn is included in A. Rademaker, *Kabinet van Nederlandsche Outheden*, 1725, p. 103. Although there is some resemblance between this and the mill depicted by Rembrandt—both for instance have the circular balcony—the features are not distinctive enough for any conclusion to be drawn.

125 (?) REMBRANDT VAN RIJN, 1606–1669

An unknown Woman

Panel (Oak), 23 × 18½ in.

SIGNED: *RHL* (in monogram).

COLL: Sir Berkeley Sheffield sale, Christie's, 16 July 1943, lot 108: bt. by Betts; date of acquisition by Lord Bearsted unrecorded.

LIT: anonymous article, 'A new Rembrandt Portrait', *Burlington Magazine*, LXXXIV, 1944, pp. 62–63, repd.; J. G. van Gelder, 'Rembrandt and his Circle', *Burlington Magazine*, XCV, 1953, p. 37.

EXH: Slatter Galleries, London, *Masterpieces of Dutch Painting*, 1945, No. 17; R.A., Winter, *Dutch Pictures*, 1952, No. 83; Whitechapel, 1955, No. 27 (Pl. XII in catalogue).

A young woman, head and shoulders, facing half left, eyes turned to front and looking slightly down; she wears a dark dress with a brown scarf fastened by a jewel, and two strings of porphyry-coloured beads.

According to the Upton catalogue the picture was certified by Tancred Borenius. There was no dissent from the attribution to Rembrandt until van Gelder published a review of the Royal Academy exhibition (*op. cit.*) in which he referred to the Upton portrait as having been painted in an imitation of Rembrandt's style, either by de Grebber or by some unknown pupil working in Amsterdam, *c*. 1634. The attribution is here left in doubt, but there is a certain lack of distinction about this portrait which favours van Gelder's view of it being the work of a follower. (The monogram form of signature is found in early works. In the present instance it appears to be suspiciously weak and may be a later addition.)

126 JACOB VAN RUISDAEL, 1628/9–1682

Le Coup de Soleil (*Plate IVb*)

Canvas, 15¾ × 16⅛ in. (approx. ¼ in. at sides and bottom painted on lining canvas).

SIGNED: *J. v. Ruisdael* (*JvR* in monogram).

COLL: Count de Morny sale, Phillips's, 20 June 1848, lot 39; Holford Collection by 1851; Sir George Holford sale, Christie's, 17 May 1928, lot 40, repd.: bt. by Knoedler, from whom acquired by Lord Bearsted.

LIT: Waagen, vol. II, p. 202 (Holford); H. de Groot, 1912, vol. IV, No. 70 (as on panel); *The Holford Collection, Dorchester House*, Oxford, 1927, vol. II, p. 32, No. 155, Pl. CXL; J. Rosenberg, *Jakob van Ruisdael*, Berlin, 1928, pp. 57–58, 75, No. 55.

EXH: B.I., 1851, No. 66; R.A., Winter, 1887, No. 109; B.F.A.C., 1900, No. 28; R.A., Winter, *17th Century Art in Europe*, 1938, No. 254; Arts Council, *Dutch Paintings of the 17th Century*, 1945, No. 29; Whitechapel, 1955, No. 35.

RELATED PICTURE: the copy mentioned by de Groot (*op. cit.*) in the Cook Collection (cf. J. O. Kronig, *Catalogue of Pictures at Doughty House*, London, 1914, vol. II, No. 347) shows a different view to the present picture.

A view from the dunes of Overveen towards Haarlem, with the Grote Kerk standing out on the horizon; nearer the foreground a castle, left, and windmill, right, and cottages among trees; beyond lies the flat landscape, momentarily lit by the sun breaking through rain clouds.

Related by Rosenberg (*op. cit.*, pp. 57–58) to a series of similar flat landscapes which he dates *c.* 1670. Other pictures belonging to this group are in the Bottenwieser (ex-Huldschinky) collection (Rosenberg, No. 41), the Mauritshuis (Rosenberg, No. 48), the Kaiser Friedrich Museum (Rosenberg, No. 39) and the Rijksmuseum (Rosenberg, No. 38).

127 SALOMON VAN RUYSDAEL, 1600/3–1670

A Country Road

Panel (Oak), $15\frac{1}{2} \times 22\frac{3}{4}$ in.

SIGNED AND DATED: *SVR* (*VR* in monogram) *1636*

COLL: previous history and date of acquisition by Lord Bearsted unrecorded.

LIT: W. Stechow, *Salomon van Ruysdael*, Berlin, 1931, p. 96, No. 241.

EXH: Whitechapel, 1955, No. 26.

A sunlit landscape with a rough road lined with trees, at the corner of which three figures are conversing; a peasant and peasant woman are resting by a bank in the foreground, and to the right is a cottage among trees; a town in the distance, left.

The monogram is somewhat lacking in assurance and may not be genuine. The attribution however appears convincing enough, although the possibility does exist that it may be by a close follower such as Pieter Nolpe.

128 PIETER JANSZ SAENREDAM, 1597–1665

The Interior of the Church of St. Catherine, Utrecht (*Plate IIIa*)

Panel (Oak), $46 \times 37\frac{3}{4}$ in.

COLL: as suggested by Swillens (*infra*) probably in the Johan Steyn Schepen sale (Haarlem, 28 April 1711). Hoet's description (*Catalogus . . . van Schilderyen*, vol. I, 1752) of lot 14 in this sale is *De Sinte Catharine Kerk tot Uytregt van Saanredam, door van Nikkelen gestoffert*. The subsequent history until this appearance of the picture at Drouot, Paris, 1928, is untraced; thence with Duits, Amsterdam, and Goudstikker; Lord Bearsted by 1929.

LIT: E. A. van Beresteyn, *Geschiedenis der Johanniter Orde in Nederland tot 1795*, The Hague, 1934, Pl. 5: P.T.A. Swillens, *Pieter Janszoon Saenredam*, Amsterdam, 1935, p. 130, No. 222, Pl. 177; W. Stechow, article in Thieme-Becker, *Künstler-Lexikon*, 1935, vol. XXIX, p. 307 (Supplement to list by H. Jantzen, *Das Niederländische Architektturbild*, 1910, pp. 168–69); S. J. Gudlaugsson, 'Aanvullingen omtrent Pieter Post's Werkzaamheid als Schilder', *Oud Holland*, LXIX, 1954, p. 66, note 15; D. Sutton, 'The Bearsted Collection', *Country Life*, CXVII, 1955, p. 871; *Catalogue Raisonné* (published in conjunction with Saenredam Exhibition, Utrecht), 1961, No. 130.

EXH: Manchester Art Gallery, *Dutch Old Masters*, 1929, No. 44; R.A., Winter, *Dutch Art*, 1929, No. 72 (*Commemorative Catalogue*, p. 121); R.A., Winter, *17th Century Art in Europe*, 1938, No. 153; Whitechapel, 1955, No. 24.

RELATED DRAWING: an approximately similar view, taken from nearer the crossing, with slight variations and without figures, inscribed and dated 20 October 1636, is in the Town Archives, Utrecht (cf. Swillens, *op. cit.*, p. 106, No. 128, Pl. 176; No. 25 in Hofstede de Groot's *Utrechtsche Kerken*, 1899).

A view of the nave and left aisle of the church, looking towards the east end, with the choir beyond and a preacher and small congregation; two kneeling men are inscribing a stone in the left foreground and six figures are disposed about the nave and aisle.

According to the Upton catalogue the picture was certified by Hofstede de Groot as the work of Saenredam. Swillens, in support of his identification with lot 14 in the Schepen sale, which according to Hoet had the figures added by van Nickelen, adduces that the fashion of the men's dress belongs to the late 1660's. Isaak van Nickelen (d. 1703) who was probably a pupil of Saenredam's, joined the Haarlem Guild in 1660. Sutton also regards the figures as having been added later.

Saenredam was in Utrecht in 1636, when he made a number of highly sensitive drawings of the churches in that town. It was his custom to use these drawings at subsequent periods in his life in order to assist in working up cartoons. From these cartoons he produced his finished paintings. In view of this practice it is unlikely that a date for the present picture can be postulated with any certainty, but if the supposition that it was finished by van Nickelen is correct, the inference is that it belongs to a late period of Saenredam's life. The intermediate cartoon in this instance is missing.

The figures in Saenredam's pictures are sometimes by other artists and the attribution of the figures in this case to van Nickelen seems likely. They have a close analogy with the stone engraver and two priests in the signed picture by that artist of the interior of St. Bavo, Haarlem (Müller sale, 28 November 1911). The area immediately surrounding the stone engravers in the present painting, and the pentiments of the architecture appearing through most of the figures, also lend support to the theory that they have been added later.

Gudlaugsson attributes the completion of the picture to van Nickelen. The possibility of it being left unfinished by Saenredam, the majority of whose pictures are signed, could account for the absence of a signature.

The Church of St. Catherine, founded in 1470 for the Carmelites and completed in 1551 after being transferred to the knights of St. John, was restored in the late nineteenth century and is now the Roman Catholic Archiepiscopal Cathedral.

129 GODFRIED SCHALCKEN, 1643–1706

Boys flying Kites

Panel (Oak), $17\frac{1}{2} \times 13\frac{1}{2}$ in.

COLL: Schamp d'Avershoot sale, Ghent, 14 September 1840, lot 116, as by Maes; Lord Aldenham sale, Sotheby's, 24 February 1937, lot 115, as by Maes: bt. by Pawsey and Payne. Date of acquisition by Lord Bearsted unrecorded.

EXH: Whitechapel, 1955, No. 37.

A polder landscape with, left, a group of three boys, two seated on the ground, one of whom has his back to the spectator and is flying a kite; the third stands between them holding a kite; another boy is running past this group, also flying a kite; on the right yellow irises are in flower.

First catalogued as by Schalcken in the Upton catalogue and previously attributed to Maes. When compared with an analogous work such as *The Angler* (Berlin, Kaiser Friedrich Museum, No. 837), which is signed by Schalcken, there is no doubt that the present attribution is the correct one.

130 JAN STEEN, 1625/6–1679

The Tired Traveller (*Plate IIId*)

Panel (Oak), $12\frac{1}{2} \times 9\frac{3}{4}$ in.

SIGNED: *J. Steen* (*JS* in monogram).

COLL: according to the Tuffen sale catalogue in the collection of the Duc de Valentinois (i.e. Prince de Carignan). It was not however included in this owner's sale, 18 June 1743. J. F. Tuffen sale, Christie's, 11 April 1818, lot 100: bt. by Pinney; Sir Simon Clarke by 1819; his sale, Christie's, 9 May 1840, lot 100: bt. by Bevan; noted by Smith (*Supplement*, 1842) as owned by Henry Bevan; entered the collection of Alfred de Rothschild subsequent to 1884 (not included in the catalogue by C. Davis published in that year) but prior to 1902 (cf. article in *Connoisseur*, *infra*); with Knoedler in 1924, from whom acquired by Lord Bearsted.

LIT: Smith, 1833, vol. IV, No. 112; and *Supplement*, 1842, No. 107; J. van Westrheene, *Jan Steen*, The Hague, 1856, p. 126, No. 117; Mrs. Erskine, 'Collection of Alfred de Rothschild', *Connoisseur*, III, 1902, p. 73; H. de Groot, 1907, vol. I, No. 668; A. Bredius, *Jan Steen*, Amsterdam, 1927, vol. II, p. 56; W. Martin, 'Neues über Jan Steen', *Zeitschrift für Bildende Kunst*, LXI, 1927–28, pp. 332, repd., 336; E. Trautscholdt, article in Thieme-Becker, *Künstler-Lexikon*, 1937, vol. XXXI, p. 513; C. H. de Jonge, *Jan Steen*, 1940, pp. 48–49; W. Martin, *Jan Steen*, Amsterdam, 1954, p. 48, Pl. 42.

EXH: B.I., 1819, No. 107; Leiden, Stedelijk Museum, *Jan Steen Memorial Exhibition*, 1926, No. 63; Manchester Art Gallery, *Dutch Old Masters*, 1929, No. 29; R.A., Winter, *Dutch Art*, 1929, No. 195. (*Commemorative Catalogue*, p. 127, Pl. LXX); Slatter Galleries, London, *Masterpieces of Dutch Painting*, 1945, No. 26 (repd. in catalogue); Birmingham Art Gallery, *Some Dutch Cabinet Pictures of the 17th Century*, 1950, No. 60; Whitechapel, 1955, No. 29 (Pl. VIII in catalogue).

ENGRAVED: by J. E. Marcus, 1813 (cf. Westrheene, *op. cit.*, p. 181, No. 48).

RELATED PICTURE: a similar scene, but viewed from a greater distance (according to Smith, *op. cit.*, of inferior quality), is in the Montpellier Museum, formerly Valedau collection (repd. by Martin in *Zeitschrift für Bildende Kunst*, p. 332).

RELATED DRAWING: a copy by A. de Frey (cf. Westrheene, p. 176, No. 72) was in the collection of M. van Willigen, Haarlem, in 1856.

In the garden of a country inn a traveller sits on a barrel under the shade of a vine-covered trellis; on the table before him is a rose, apparently intended for the servant girl, wearing a lemon-coloured bodice and blue skirt, who offers him a glass of wine from a flagon she holds in her right hand. (*Pentimenti* by the man's left leg and table leg.)

Martin (*Zeitschrift*, p. 336) dates the picture *c.* 1665, about ten years later than the Montpellier version.

131 JAN STEEN, 1625/26–1679

The Sense of Hearing

Panel (Oak), $10\frac{1}{8} \times 8\frac{1}{2}$ in.

SIGNED: *J. Steen* (*JS* in monogram).

COLL: according to Hofstede de Groot the set of the *Five Senses* appeared in an anonymous sale at Amsterdam in 1695 and was then in the Borwater and van Breemen sales. Hoet's references (*Catalogus of Naamlyst van Schilderyen*, 3 vols., 1752–70) would seem to confirm this, though not explicit enough for certain identification: anonymous sale, Amsterdam, 6 April 1695, lot 12 (Hoet, vol. I, p. 22: *De Vyf Sinnen van Jan Steen, in vyf stukken*); A. Borwater sale, The Hague, 20 July 1756, lot 79 (Hoet, vol. III, p. 156: *Vyf stukjes, zynde de Vyf Sinnen, door Jan Steen*); N. van Breemen sale, The Hague, 3 April 1769 (no lot number; Hoet, vol. II, p. 484: *Vyf Stuks, verbeeldende de Vyf Sinne, door David Teniers ieder h 10d., br. 8 en een vierde d.*). Four of the series (those now at Upton, i.e. less the *Sense of Touch*, the whereabouts of which has has not been discovered) were sold by A. T. Ross at Sotheby's, 3 November 1926, lot 107. The catalogue entry of this sale described the pictures as having belonged to Prince Leopold and sold at the 'Boyle Farm Sale'. This has not been substantiated but is borne out by labels on the backs of Nos. 131 and 134. In 1928 the four pictures were with Goudstikker, Amsterdam, and are thus referred to by Trautscholdt in Thieme-Becker (1937). Date of acquisition by Lord Bearsted unrecorded. (The number *248* is painted in the right bottom corner of No. 131.)

LIT: J. van Westrheene, *Jan Steen*, The Hague, 1856, p. 156, No. 437; H. de Groot, 1907, vol. I, Nos. 104–8; E. Trautscholdt, article in Thieme-Becker, *Künstler-Lexikon*, 1937, vol. XXXI, p. 511.

EXH: Whitechapel, 1955, No. 30.

ENGRAVED: by J. Gole (cf. F. Hollstein,

Dutch and Flemish Etching, Engraving and Woodcuts, Amsterdam, 1952, vol. VII, No. 274).

COMPANION PICTURES: Nos. 132–4.

A seated peasant wearing a jerkin over a red blouse with grey breeches and scarlet hat is singing from a music score which he holds in his left hand, while his right is raised beating time; on the table by his side is a flagon, and two musical instruments hang on the wall behind.

132 JAN STEEN, 1625/26–1679

The Sense of Taste

Panel (Oak), $10\frac{1}{8} \times 8\frac{1}{8}$ in.

SIGNED: *J. Steen* (*JS* in monogram).

COLL: cf. No. 131 (the number 24(?)4 is painted in the corner).

LIT: cf. No. 131.

EXH: Whitechapel, 1955, No. 31.

ENGRAVED: cf. No. 131 (Hollstein, *op. cit.*, No. 272).

COMPANION PICTURES: Nos. 131, 133–4.

A peasant wearing a blue coat, brown breeches and white cap seated on a chair with an earthenware bowl of soup on his knees, lifting a wooden spoon to his mouth with his right hand.

133 JAN STEEN, 1625/26–1679

The Sense of Smell

Panel (Oak), $10 \times 8\frac{1}{8}$ in.

SIGNED: *J. Steen* (*JS* in monogram).

COLL: cf. No. 131. (The number *239* is painted in the corner.)

LIT: cf. No. 131.

EXH: Whitechapel, 1955, No. 32.

ENGRAVED: cf. No. 131: (Hollstein, *op. cit.*, No. 271).

COMPANION PICTURES: Nos. 131–2, 134.

A young peasant wearing brown, with grey jerkin and large grey hat, seated, leaning his left arm on the back of a chair and holding a long clay pipe to his mouth with his right hand; on a table beside him is a jug.

Plate IIIa Saenredam (128)

Plate IIIb Van der Heyden (118)

Plate IIIc Metsu (120)

Plate IIId Steen (130)

Plate IV a Meurant (122)

Plate IV b Ruisdael (126)

Plate IV c Van Goyen (117)

Plate IV d Cappelle (111)

134 JAN STEEN, 1625/26–1679

The Sense of Sight

Panel (Oak), $10\frac{1}{8} \times 8\frac{1}{8}$ in.

SIGNED: *J. Steen* (*JS* in monogram).

COLL: cf. No. 131 (the number *241* is painted in the corner).

LIT: cf. No. 131.

EXH: Whitechapel, 1955, No. 33.

ENGRAVED: cf. No. 131 (Hollstein, *op. cit.*, No. 270).

COMPANION PICTURES: Nos. 131–3.

A peasant wearing grey with a large brown hat, seated on a bench, looking into an empty jug which he tips up and holds with both hands.

135 ADRIAEN PIETERSZ VAN DER VENNE, 1589–1662

Peasants dancing

Panel (Oak), $11\frac{7}{8} \times 14\frac{5}{8}$ in. (*Grisaille*).

SIGNED AND DATED: *AP v. Venne 1633* (*AP* in monogram).

INSCRIBED: *Goed Rond* (on scroll).

COLL: anonymous sale, Christie's, 15 May 1936, lot 99: bt. by Martin for Lord Bearsted.

RELATED PICTURES: a number of *grisaille* scenes of dancing peasants, etc., with similar forms of inscription, were painted by van der Venne at varying dates after he had settled at The Hague in 1625. Often these were didactic or moralizing in their nature.

A landscape with a stormy sky. Ten peasants are dancing in a ring to a flautist who stands at the left; in the distance, right, a church tower.

137 GERARD VAN HONTHORST, 1590–1656

An unknown Man

Panel (Oak), $25\frac{1}{4} \times 22\frac{1}{4}$ in.

INSCRIBED: *G. Honthorst*

COLL: according to the Upton catalogue in the collection of the Earl of Romney in 1895. This may be mistaken since only the portraits of Frederick V and Elizabeth of Bohemia (see below) were included in his sale at Christie's in that year. Date of acquisition by Lord Bearsted unrecorded, but before 1929.

Head and shoulders to right, head facing, wearing armour with a pale crimson sash and lace collar; long hair and moustache.

At a sale of pictures belonging to Lord Bearsted (Christie's, 13 December 1929) the present portrait (lot 84) was bought in. A series of portraits by Honthorst, on canvas, similar in composition and similarly inscribed with the name of the artist, but in sculptured ovals and signed and dated from 1637–39, were sold as lots 78–83, and a panel, the same size as the present picture, was sold as lot 85. Other than the portraits of Frederick V and Elizabeth of Bohemia these were catalogued as unknown sitters. The present picture was also included in a sale at Christie's, 26 May 1933, lot 48, but once again was unsold.

136 PHILIPS WOUVERMANS, 1619–1668

A Landscape with Dunes and Figures

Canvas, $26\frac{1}{2} \times 22$ in.

SIGNED: *Philips W* (*Philips* in monogram).

COLL: according to the Upton catalogue the picture came from the collections of H. Menier (Paris, 15 March 1914) and M. Kappel, Berlin. These sales have not been substantiated nor is the date of entry in the Upton collection known. The picture is not included in *Die Gemäldesammlung Marcus Kappel* (W. von Bode, Berlin, 1914).

In the centre on a dune is a tumble-down shelter, partly supported by two trees; to the right a cart, near which is a dog and two cows, while part of a thatched cottage is seen further right. A path runs along the foot of the dune and in the centre a horseman has halted; a dog jumps up at him, and to the left a foot traveller kneels to attend to a second dog; left, two figures at a bend in the path, and in the distance a river or lake with hills beyond; a stormy sky.

137 (Honthorst) will be found preceding No. 136 (Wouvermans).

C

Flemish and Early Netherlandish Schools

143 HIERONYMUS BOSCH, active
1480/81–1516

The Adoration of the Magi (Triptych)
(*Plate Vb*)

Panel (Oak), Centre panel: 35 × 26¾ in.;
Wings (each): 34¾ × 11⅜ in. (irregularly
shaped top.)

COLL: H. D. Seymour, 1854; by descent in the
family; Miss Seymour sale, Knight, Frank &
Rutley, 17 January 1936, lot 324: bt. by
Langton Douglas; acquired by Lord Bearsted
by 1937.

LIT: Waagen, 1854, vol. II, p. 243 (Seymour);
W. Cohen, article in Thieme-Becker, *Künstler-
Lexikon*, 1910, vol. IV, p. 389; P. Lafond,
Hieronymus Bosch, Paris, 1914, pp. 39, 111;
Friedländer, 1937, vol. XIV, pp. 99–100,
No. 68; X. de Salas, 'Cronica de Londres',
Goya, VI, 1955, p. 366.

EXH: Whitechapel, 1955, No. 75 (Pl. XXXV in
catalogue).

RELATED PICTURES: the centre panel of the
present picture is a variant of the *Adoration*
in the Prado, Madrid (No. 2084), which is
dated by Friedländer c. 1495. The main
difference is that in the Prado altarpiece the
landscape is extended considerably above the
stable. A list of six other versions or copies is
included by Friedländer under the catalogue
entry No. 68 (p. 144) of vol. V of *Altniederländische Malerei*. Another version of the
central panel is at Petworth (Collins Baker,
Catalogue, 1920, pp. 8–9, No. 63) and further
versions are given in C. de Tolnay, *Hieronymus
Bosch*, Basle, 1937, p. 99, No. 31. The compositions on both sides of the wings of the present
triptych do not occur in any of the other works,
although the right wing of a triptych attributed
to Bosch in the Johnson collection, Philadelphia
(W. R. Valentiner, *Catalogue*, 1913, vol. II,
No. 354) shows a group of horsemen representing the arrival of the Magi. The lost
central panel of the Johnson picture, depicting
the *Adoration of the Magi* (known through a
copy), is a composition unrelated to the Prado
series.

Centre Panel: as has been said this is essentially
the same as the Prado *Epiphany* except for a

difference of proportion: here the gable of the
shed breaks the horizon and the incidents in
the background are less numerous and varied.
The Madonna and Child are isolated from the
group of kings by the curved trunk of a tree.
The second king wears a chasuble, the collar of
which is decorated with a scene showing the
Queen of Sheba before Solomon (a prototype
of the Adoration). Balthasar, the Moorish king,
in a white dalmatic, carries an orb again
decorated with an exemplar of the Adoration,
the Three Heroes offering water to David. The
figure in the doorway, one of whose identities
may, as Mrs. Philip suggests (see below) be
Antichrist, wears a metal turban of thorns
and a budding twig, symbolizing Antichrist's
mutation of the life and passion of Christ and
his trick of making a dead branch blossom. The
ass (symbolizing the old law) is seen un-
accompanied by the ox (symbol of the new law)
and thus the pagan world only is represented.
The subject of Gaspar's gift, lying at the feet
of the Madonna, is unidentified and differs from
its counterpart in the Prado picture, a model of
the Sacrifice of Isaac (typifying the sacrifice of
Christ). There is a pentiment along the left
edge of the stable roof.

Right Wing: the mounted retinue of the kings,
carrying three lances with pennants, in a
landscape with a conduit in the foreground.
They look upwards as if at the star (not visible
in the picture) while one of them kneels on the
ground handling what appears to be a large
portfolio.

Left Wing: St. Joseph kneels in the foreground
gathering sticks and water, the Child's bath-tub
beside him; behind him is a ruined palace,
with a table, bench and fire visible through an
arcade, and the half-length statue of a prophet
above the central column. (*Pentimenti* in the
circular tower of the palace, and in the form of
a building in the landscape.)

Verso: when closed the wings display a central
roundel with Christ before Pilate after the
Flagellation: Christ, wearing a robe and crown
of thorns, is seen half-length on the left,
handled by the executioners, with Pilate
opposite him surrounded by heads in turbans

and helmets; two of these seem to correspond with figures in the doorway of the stable in the centre panel. The surrounding areas are painted in *grisaille* and show a scene with demons flying in the air and a procession of fantastic figures, some mounted, hurrying along the ground to the left, where a gallows beset with demons is erected beside a cylindrical building.

It is clear that this picture contains a wealth of allusions, and in an article in the *Art Bulletin* (XXV, 1953, pp. 267–93) Lotte Brand Philip has provided an interpretation of the symbolism and a solution of all the obscure passages in the Prado *Epiphany*. The traditional features of the *Adoration of the Magi* are here regarded as veiling a microcosm of the predominantly evil world. The development of the theme and its didactic nature, as it is traced by Mrs. Philip in the background of the central panel and throughout every incident in the wings, concluding with an exegesis of the exterior scenes, is not applicable to the Upton version, where only the centre group corresponds, although with minor differences, to the Prado altarpiece.

In the Upton catalogue two letters from Dr. Friedländer are quoted, one dated 14 July 1936 after he had seen the wings, and the second dated 1 September 1936 after having seen the complete triptych in Berlin.

Dr. Friedländer's opinion is that the triptych is an autograph work by Bosch, probably repeated for a commission: 'Kolorit, Zeichnung und Ausdruck stehen auf derselben Höhe wie in dem Madrider Gemälde.' He alludes to it in *Altniederländische Malerei* as a free replica of the middle panel of the Prado *Epiphany*, with different compositions on the wings and *verso*. Cohen refers to the picture as an old copy, Lafond as a variant, and de Salas as possibly from the workshop of Bosch. The attribution to the master given in the Upton catalogue is followed here. It must however be emphasized that No. 143, despite the difficulty of judging it in its present damaged condition, is not comparable in quality with the Prado *Epiphany*.

144 Attributed to AELBRECHT BOUTS, active 1473–1549

The Madonna and Child

Panel (Oak), $12\frac{1}{8} \times 9\frac{5}{8}$ in.

COLL: C. L. Cardon in 1906; his sale, Brussels, 27 June 1921, lot 23, repd., as by Hugo van der Goes; date of acquisition by Lord Bearsted unrecorded.

LIT: H. Hymans, 'L'Exposition de la Toison d'Or à Bruges', *Gazette des Beaux-Arts*, 1907 (II), pp. 210–12; L. Dumont-Wilden, 'La Collection de M. Cardon', *Les Arts*, VIII, 1909, pp. 2, 16 (repd.).

EXH: Guildhall, *Flemish Painters*, 1906, No. 15; Bruges, *La Toison d'Or*, 1907, No. 190; Brussels, Hotel Goffinet, *La Miniature*, 1912, No. 2011; Whitechapel, 1955, No. 79.

The Madonna, half length, wearing a blue robe and blue and white headdress, holds the naked Child against her right shoulder; in His left hand He holds an apple on His knee. The background is formed by a red curtain.

The attribution to van der Goes remained with the picture until it appeared in the Upton catalogue as by Albert Bouts. Hymans, who regarded it as probably of Bruges origin, pointed out the relationship between this panel (which he referred to as No. 189 instead of No. 190 when writing of the *Toison d'Or* exhibition) and an engraving by the Master WX (practising in Bruges, *c.* 1465–85) showing the *Madonna and Child before a Gothic window* (M. Lehrs, *Der Meister WX*, Leipzig, 1895, No. 2: cf. also No. 3).

However the composition seems to derive from the Virgin in Rogier van der Weyden's picture of *St. Luke Painting the Virgin*, of which several versions are known, and from which the Madonna and Child were repeated as separate compositions by Rogier himself (e.g. in the Renders collection) and as variants by some of his followers.

The facial type of the Madonna in the present picture is close in style to Albert Bouts, and the attribution to this artist given in the Upton catalogue is tentatively retained here.

145 BOUTS, DIRK
See *Rogier van der Weyden (Follower of)*

146 BOUTS, DIRK
See *Rogier van der Weyden (Follower of)*

147 BOUTS, DIRK
See *Master of the St. Lucy Legend*

148 (Pieter Brueghel the Elder) will be found following No. 150 (Style of Jan Brueghel the Younger).

149 BRUEGHEL, JAN THE ELDER

See *Brueghel, Pieter (After)*

172 Style of JAN BRUEGHEL THE ELDER, 1568–1625

A Harbour Scene

Metal, $10\frac{5}{8} \times 14$ in.

COLL: R. A. Ogilby sale, Christie's, 28 April 1922, lot 61: bt. by Sabin (with No. 173); date of acquisition by Lord Bearsted unrecorded.

A river estuary with boats moored along the beach near a village which lines the right bank; groups of figures are gathered in the foreground in front of a windmill on a dune, while a sailing boat, laden with passengers, is being drawn up to the shore.

Sold as a pair with No. 173 in 1922, but by a different hand and somewhat superior. The scene is characteristic: cf. e.g. an engraving by Aegidius Sadeler after Brueghel (repd. H. and M. Ogden, *English Taste in Landscape in the 17th Century*, Michigan, 1955, p. 185, fig. 12) which shows a similar view.

173 Style of JAN BRUEGHEL THE ELDER, 1568–1625

A Village Scene

Metal, $12\frac{1}{2} \times 9$ in.

COLL: cf. No. 172.

RELATED PICTURES: a similar view of this village occurs, with variations, in other pictures attributed to Jan Brueghel the Elder or Younger: e.g., cf. Christie's, 9 July 1937, lot 19, from the collection of Major Curtis.

A wide village street with scattered figures and carts and a group of figures conversing in the left foreground; beyond the village an extensive view over flat country.

Sold as a pair with No. 172 in 1922, but apparently by a different hand.

150 Style of JAN BRUEGHEL THE YOUNGER, 1601–1678

A Cottage among Trees

Metal, $5\frac{7}{8} \times 8\frac{1}{4}$ in.

COLL: previous history and date of acquisition by Lord Bearsted unrecorded.

A cottage stands in a clearing in a wood. In the foreground, two peasants are conversing, the woman wearing a red skirt, the man a red jacket. (Formerly entitled *Summer*.)

The previous unequivocal attribution to Jan Brueghel the Younger, while reasonably convincing, is nevertheless difficult to uphold and is therefore qualified here.

148 PIETER BRUEGHEL THE ELDER, active 1551–1569

The Dormition of the Virgin (*Plate Va*)

Panel (Oak), $14\frac{1}{2} \times 21\frac{7}{8}$ in. (*Grisaille*.)

SIGNED: *Bruegel* (indistinct traces of a date).

COLL: the hypothesis that the picture had once belonged to the famous geographer, Abraham Ortelius (1527–98), who commissioned the engraving, was confirmed by Popham (see below). It is likely to have been owned by Rubens, in all probability being the picture listed as No. 193 in the inventory taken after his death in 1641: *De Dood van de H. Maegd, in het graeuw, door denzelven* (i.e., *Ouden Breughel*), specified as having been the property of Rubens's first wife (cf. J. F. M. Michel, *Histoire de la Vie de P. P. Rubens*, Brussels, 1771, p. 282). Later it may have been in the collection of Joan Baptista Anthoine, Antwerp, among whose effects is listed (10 April 1691), *Pinnel den Sterffdach van onse lieve Vrouwe, Breughel* (cf. *Antwerpsch Archievenblad*, XXII, p. 78). It next appears two hundred and forty years later, being discovered c. 1930 by Vitale Bloch in the English art trade. In 1930 it was in the possession of Lord Lee of Fareham, from whom it was acquired by Lord Bearsted the same year.

LIT: L. Burchard, *Unknown Masterpieces* (ed. Valentiner), London, 1930, No. 40, repd.; W. G. Constable, 'Northern Painting in the Lee Collection', *International Studio*, March 1930, pp. 41, repd., 43; G. Glück, 'A newly-discovered Painting by Pieter Brueghel', *Burlington Magazine*, LVI, 1930, pp. 284ff., repd.; A. E. Popham, 'Pieter Bruegel and Abraham Ortelius', *Burlington Magazine*, LIX, 1931, pp. 184–8; E. Michel, *Bruegel*, Paris, 1931, pp. 85–86, Pl. 58; G. Glück, *Brueghel's Gemälde*, Vienna, 1932, p. 62, No. 16 repd.; C. de Tolnay, *Pierre Bruegel L'Ancien*, Brussels, 1935, pp. 51–52, 92, No. 38, Pl. 148; Friedländer, 1937, vol. XIV, pp. 29, 60, No. 23, Pl. XXIII; G. Glück, *Pieter Brueghel the Elder*, London, 1951,

No. 20, repd.; F. Grossmann, 'Bruegel's Woman taken in Adultery and other Grisailles', *Burlington Magazine*, XCIV, 1952, pp. 221ff (*passim*), repd., p. 227, No. 6; D. Sutton, 'Flemish Painting at the Royal Academy', *Les Arts Plastiques*, VI, 1954, pp. 23–26; F. Grossmann, *Bruegel: The Paintings*, London, 1955, p. 196, No. 77, Pl. 77.

EXH: on loan to National Gallery, London, 1938–47; R.A., Winter, *Flemish Art*, 1953, No. 309; Whitechapel, 1955, No. 88 (Pl. XXVIII in catalogue); Musée Communal, Bruges, *L'Art Flamand dans les Collections Britanniques*, 1956, No. 54 (Pl. 38 in catalogue).

ENGRAVED: by Philip Galle, 1574 (in same direction as painting); commissioned by Abraham Ortelius. The inscription on the print reads: *sic Petri Brugelij archetypu(m) Phillip, Gallaeus imitabatur; R: Abrah. Ortelius sibi et amicis fieri curabat*. The verses accompanying this inscription are transcribed by Grossmann (*Burlington Magazine*). The engraving is reproduced by R. van Bastelaer and Hulin de Loo, *Pieter Bruegel L'Ancien*, Brussels, 1907, p. 126 (catalogued p. 236, No. 116). Before the discovery of the painting, Hulin de Loo (*op. cit.*, p. 331, B.13) noted that the original of the engraving would prove to be a *grisaille* with the composition in the same sense. F. Winkler, *Altniederländische Malerei*, Berlin, 1924, p. 338, suggested, also before the painting was discovered, that the engraving was taken from a lost *early* work by Brueghel. This use of *grisaille* for the engraver to copy may have influenced Rubens, who adopted a similar practice.

RELATED PICTURE: a repetition in colour was sold with Edouard Fétis' collection, Brussels, 1909, lot 11, repd.

The interior of a room at night. The Virgin sits up in bed and receives a lighted taper from (?)St. Peter, who stands right, wearing a chasuble, amongst a group of kneeling Disciples; the (?)Magdalen, opposite, smoothes her pillows. Many other figures crowd towards the bed from the left side of the room and from the door in the background; in the left foreground a man who may be St. John sleeps in a chair near the fire; at the foot of the bed, where a crucifix is laid upon a pillow, a kneeling monk rings the passing bell, and in the centre foreground a bench, chair and round table are covered with an assortment of plates and cups. The room is unevenly lit from four sources: the fire, the torches placed high up on a carved wooden frieze between the bed and the door, a candle

on the table and the taper held by St. Peter. The back of the panel is inscribed, *Ouden Pr Brueghel 1(?)42*. (According to Mr. H. Hardenberg of the Algemeen Rijksarchief at The Hague, this is a late eighteenth- or early nineteenth-century script.)

The ownership of Ortelius was confirmed when Popham (*op. cit.*) discovered amongst the geographer's correspondence a letter from the Spanish biblical scholar, Benedictus Arias Montanus (1527–98), written from Seville on 30 March 1590, in which a painting of the *Death of the Virgin*, engraved by Philip Galle, was mentioned as being in Ortelius's house.

Glück, writing in the *Burlington Magazine*, suggests a late date of *c.* 1564, with which Grossmann concurs. The *terminus ante quem* supplied by Montanus's letter is unhelpful in dating the picture, since Montanus had only lived in Antwerp from 1568, leaving for Spain in 1575.

Tolnay and Michel, who do not regard the picture as an autograph work, are understandably not followed in this opinion by the other authors quoted above. The former considers the handling uncharacteristic and as a further point draws attention to an error of perspective in the chair, which has been corrected in the engraving (cf. Grossmann, *Burlington Magazine* (p. 223, note 16) for a refutation of this point). According to Michel the treatment of the light indicates that the picture may be a later copy.

Glück (*Burlington Magazine*) describes the iconographic novelty of the composition: whereas previously the mourners had always been limited to the apostolic number of twelve, the subject is now treated by Brueghel as a natural event, to which numerous men and women are admitted (cf. verses accompanying engraving). Grossmann (1952) refers to the death of the Virgin as a phenomenon in which all the righteous take part. He expands this (1955), mentioning as the source of the composition the *Golden Legend* of Jacobus de Voragine. In the account given in an apocryphal book of St. John the Evangelist, Christ with the patriarchs, martyrs, confessors and holy virgins are described as being present at the death of the Virgin, where the Apostles are already assembled. Grossmann suggests that St. John is shown asleep and isolated as the recorder of the miracle.

However Brueghel does not appear to be influenced by the supernatural features of this part of the story, and his interpretation of the scene is factual enough for it to be questioned whether he had this special mystical significance in mind. It may therefore be, as Glück suggested, that Brueghel is depicting the scene straightforwardly and that St. John, having fallen asleep in exhaustion at the critical moment, is a poignant motif added by the artist.

Tolnay (*op. cit.*) writes that the inspiration for the composition is derived from a miniature, *La Mort*, in the *Grimani Breviary* (repd. by Tolnay, Pl. 153). Schongauer's influential engraving of the *Death of the Virgin* (Lehrs, *Geschichte und Kritische Katalog*, 1925, vol. V, No. 16) may also have proved a source for the group of Apostles round the bed.

149 After PIETER BRUEGHEL THE ELDER, active 1551–1569

The Massacre of the Innocents

Panel (Oak), $17\frac{1}{4} \times 25\frac{1}{2}$ in.

COLL: previous history and date of acquisition by Lord Bearsted unrecorded, but at Upton before 1923. On the building at the right of the picture is a crown surmounting a monogram (?*KAT*), which to judge from an X-ray photograph of the painting appears to be contemporary and may indicate the original owner.

EXH: B.F.A.C., 1923, No. 22.

RELATED PICTURES: this is a copy of the version of the subject in the Kunsthistorisches Museum, Vienna, generally dated 1565–67, of which a number of other copies exist. The child in the right foreground does not appear in the Vienna picture.

The picture in Vienna, formerly regarded as the original, is now thought to be a copy (cf. Friedländer, 1937, vol. XIV, p. 61, No. 37). Grossmann (*Bruegel: The Paintings*, London, 1955, Nos. 111, 113) puts forward the theory, based on X-ray photographs, that the original is the overpainted version at Hampton Court, in which the nature of the scene was altered in the seventeenth century to depict the plundering of a village.

The biblical scene is represented as a contemporary event. The massacre is perpetrated in a broad village street filled with groups of soldiers and villagers; a troop of cavalry is drawn up in the background.

Formerly catalogued as by Jan Brueghel the Elder, after Pieter Brueghel. In the absence of any justification for this attribution, and in view of the uneven quality of the picture, it seems more plausible to regard it as by an anonymous copyist, approximately contemporary with the original.

150 (Attributed to Jan Brueghel the Younger) will be found preceding No. 148 (Pieter Brueghel)

151 BURGUNDIAN FOLLOWER OF ROGIER VAN DER WEYDEN
See *Master of the St. Barbara Legend*

152 CONINXLOO, GILLIS VAN THE ELDER
See *Wtewael*

153 GERARD DAVID, active 1484–1523

The Madonna and Child (*Plate VIIc*)

Panel (Oak), Painted surface: $6\frac{1}{8} \times 4\frac{5}{8}$ in. (arched top). Size of panel, on which frame is carved, to top of finial: $9\frac{5}{8} \times 6\frac{5}{8}$ in.

COLL: Otto Kahn in 1911 (cf. Bodenhausen, *infra*) and 1931 (cf. *Apollo, infra*). In the Upton catalogue the provenance is given as Altman; Kahn; John Ford. According to Mr. Brinsley Ford the picture was never in the latter collection (i.e., John G. Ford, who with his brother Capt. Richard Ford inherited in 1899 the Ford pictures from his father, Sir Francis Clare Ford). The association with Altman may be due to confusion with the New York panel (see below) which passed from Kahn to Altman and was bequeathed by the latter to the Metropolitan Museum in 1913. According to the Museum catalogue (1947) both pictures came originally from Spain (also cf. Bodenhausen, where it is said that No. 153 was with Gimpel and Wildenstein, Paris, in the intervening period). The date of acquisition by Lord Bearsted is not recorded.

LIT: E. von Bodenhausen and W. R. Valentiner, 'Zum Werk Gerard Davids', *Zeitschrift für Bildende Kunst*, XXII, 1911, p. 185, No. 6, repd.; Friedländer, 1928, vol. VI, p. 146, No. 170, Pl. LXXVIII; *Apollo*, XIV, 1931, repd. p. 16.

EXH: R.A., Winter, *Flemish and Belgian Art*, 1927, No. 102 (*Commemorative Catalogue*, No. 102, Pl. XLVIII); Whitechapel, 1955, No. 78 (Pl. XXIX in catalogue); Musée Communal, Bruges, *L'Art Flamand dans les Collections Britanniques*, 1956, No. 23 (Pl. 15 in catalogue).

COMPANION PICTURE: the present picture is regarded by Friedländer as the left portion of a diptych, of which the other half is the *Christ taking leave of his Mother* in the Metropolitan Museum, New York (Altman Bequest). This is questioned in the 1947 museum catalogue, for the reason that although the provenance of the two pictures is similar in that they both came from Spain and then entered the Kahn collection, the scale of the figures in the New York painting is disproportionately large (also cf. M. L. d'Otrange, 'David at the Metropolitan', *Connoisseur*, CXXVIII, 1951, p. 211). There is the additional fact that the New York panel (although it may have been modified at some time) is apparently differently framed to No. 153 where the picture surface and frame are formed of one piece of wood. The two works are not linked in Bodenhausen and Valentiner, who reproduced the New York painting (p. 188, No. 11) as a late work. Similar subjects were however combined in a diptych now in the van Gelder collection at Uccle (repd. in *Commemorative Catalogue*, 1927 R.A. Exhibition, Pl. XLVIII), and also in Nos. 547–8 in the Bavarian National Museum, Munich (repd. in catalogue of Exhibition, *Gerard David*, Musée Communal, Bruges, 1949, No. 5, Pl. VII).

The Madonna, half length, wearing a blue robe and crown, holds the fair-haired Child, in a pale-mauve dress, on her right arm, and with the other hand offers Him an apple; two angels, in pale-blue robes, hover with outstretched wings on either side, playing musical instruments and looking down upon the Child. Gold background. On the reverse are areas of brush strokes on gesso, as if used as a palette or in imitation of marble (badly damaged).

Bodenhausen and Valentiner date the picture c. 1505, i.e. they regard it as approximately coeval with, or a little earlier than the *Marriage of St. Catherine* (cf. Bodenhausen, *Gerard David und seine Schule*, Munich, 1905, p. 154, No. 25). The present picture is cited as a prototype for Isenbrandt's miniature paintings (cf. a *Madonna and Child with Angels* by that artist: Bodenhausen, *op. cit.*, p. 216, No. 76, then collection Traumann, Madrid).

154 Close Follower of HUGO VAN DER GOES, active 1467–1482

The Vision of the Emperor Augustus
(*Plate VIId*)

Panel (Oak), 12 × 8⅜ in. (arched top.)

COLL: R. A. Ogilby sale, Christie's, 28 April 1922, lot 74: bt. by Sabin; date of acquisition by Lord Bearsted unrecorded.

LIT: Friedländer, 1926, vol. IV, pp. 73, 133, No. 31, Pl. XXXVII; F. M. Godfrey, 'Hugo van der Goes', *Connoisseur*, CXXVI, 1950, p. 10; K. G. Boon 'Meester van de Khanenko Aanbidding of van de Kruisiging te Turijn' *Oud Holland*, LXVIII, 1953, p. 214, fig. 6.

EXH: Whitechapel, 1955, No. 71 (Pl. XXXII in catalogue).

Half-length figures facing towards the left; the bearded emperor kneels, his hands joined in prayer, a turban supported in his arms, wearing a dark blue habit and red cloak with wide fur collar and cuffs and a gold chain round his neck. Behind him the Tiburtine Sibyl wears an embroidered grey dress and blue collar edged with gold, and green sleeves; her ornamented and jewelled headdress is decorated with the words SIBILLA R . . . In the background, seen beyond a parapet, is the courtyard of a palace with scattered figures.

According to tradition the Madonna and Child appeared to Augustus and a Sibyl and pointed out the site of S. M. d'Aracoeli in Rome. Friedländer writes (p. 73) that the companion panel of the diptych would in all probability have been the Madonna, and that the interchanging of emperor and donor, sibyl and patron saint is unprecedented. He catalogues the picture under *Followers of van der Goes* (p.133), but adds that the execution is worthy of the master himself: if not by him, it is the work of a distinguished, unknown follower. Boon connects the picture with a triptych of the *Crucifixion* at Turin (*Catalogue*, 1909, No. 362, as Engelbrechtz) and a *Crucifixion* at Frankfurt (Staedel Institute, No. 1067), previously attributed by Dülberg (*Die Frühholländer*, 1907, vol. III, pp. 15–17) and by Hoogewerff (*Noord Nederlandse Schilderkunst*, 1939, vol. III, pp. 209–10) to Huug Jacobsz, the father of Lucas van Leyden. Boon regards the anonymous artist, to whom he attributes these works, as beginning his career as an imitator of van der Goes, and developing later in Antwerp a mannerist style. He suggests that he may be the same as the so-called 'Master of the Khanenko Adoration' and that a picture such as the *Madonna* in the Stuttgart gallery (cf. Friedländer, *op. cit.*, No. 46, Pl. XLIV) might be an early work prior to the artist's Antwerp period.

If Boon's hypothesis is correct, No. 154,

which has analogies with the Stuttgart *Madonna*, could also be an early work of the master. Both the Turin and Frankfurt *Crucifixions*, as well as the two other works associated by Boon, are considerably more mannered and agitated than the present painting.

155 ABEL GRIMMER, active 1592–1619

Peasants dancing

Panel (Oak), $9\frac{1}{4} \times 15\frac{1}{8}$ in.

SIGNED: *ABEL GRIMER FECIT 16(?)14*

COLL: W. A. Coats; included in the catalogue of this owner's collection (1904, No. IX) and exhibited by him in 1927. It was not among his pictures sold at Christie's in that year (10 June) nor among those inherited by Major J. A. and T. H. Coats and sold in 1935 (Christie's, 12 April). The date of entry into Lord Bearsted's collection is unrecorded.

EXH: Royal Society of British Artists, London, *W. A. Coats Collection*, 1927, No. 149.

A landscape with a group of peasants dressed in brightly coloured clothes on a path in the foreground; those on the right are dancing to the bagpipes of a man seated behind, while on the left a well-to-do couple are walking with their children; in the background are further groups of figures.

156 ABEL GRIMMER, active 1592–1619

The Four Seasons

Panels (Oak), circular: a set of four in one frame, each 5 in. diam.

SIGNED: (I) Unsigned (II) *GRIMER FECIT* (III) *GRIMER* (IV) *ABEL GRIMER F. 1600*

COLL: previous history and date of acquisition by Lord Bearsted unrecorded.

EXH: Whitechapel, 1955, No. 89.

(I) Sheep-dipping (Spring): figures and sheep in the foreground of a village street. (II) Haymaking (Summer): figures scything and gathering hay, a town in the distance. (III) Wood-cutting (Autumn): men cutting and carting wood, a village in the background. (IV) Snow scene (Winter): a town under snow with figures in a square.

151 MASTER OF THE ST. BARBARA LEGEND, active late fifteenth century

A Man and his Wife

Panel (Oak), $15\frac{1}{2} \times 11$ in.

COLL: with the van Diemen Gallery, Berlin (repd. in *Das Kunstblatt*, VI (Heft IX), 1922, p. 369, as Burgundian School *c.* 1400 in the possession of this gallery); referred to in Hulin de Loo's article as with the London trade; acquired by Lord Bearsted by 1937.

LIT: Hulin de Loo, 'Vrancke van der Stockt', *Biographie Nationale de Belgique*, Brussels, 1926–29, vol. XXIV, p. 74; Friedländer, 1937, vol. XIV, p. 94.

EXH: Brussels, *Exposition Universelle, Cinq Siècles d'Art*, 1935, No. 31 (as Master of the Redemption of the Prado); Paris, Musée de l'Orangerie, *De Van Eyck à Brueghel*, 1935, No. 60 (as Master of the Redemption of the Prado); Whitechapel, 1955, No. 81 (Pl.XXXIV in catalogue).

They are seen half length at a window; the man faces to the left, wearing a black cloak, red sleeves slashed with white, and black hat, his hands joined in prayer, an open missal resting on the ledge in front of him. His wife stands at his left shoulder; she wears a plum coloured dress and scarlet bodice with black cuffs and lapels, a black hat with a veil falling to her shoulders; from her belt hangs a rosary which she fingers with both hands. Gold background.

Probably the right wing of a diptych. In the Upton catalogue as by a Burgundian Follower of Rogier van der Weyden. Friedländer agrees with Hulin de Loo's oral statement that the picture may be by the Master of the Barbara Legend. Previously Hulin de Loo (*op. cit.*) had ascribed it to Vrancke van der Stockt (of whom the Master of the Barbara Legend was a follower), associated by him with the Master of the Redemption of the Prado, whose eponymous picture (Prado, Nos. 1889–91) has since been identified with the so-called Cambrai altarpiece (1455–59) of Rogier van der Weyden. In the same article Hulin de Loo dates the present picture *c.* 1470.

157 Style of MASTER OF THE ST. CATHERINE LEGEND, active late fifteenth century

The Madonna and Child with an Angel

Panel (Oak). Painted surface: $8\frac{3}{4} \times 5\frac{1}{2}$ in. Size

Plate Va Brueghel (148)

Plate Vb Bosch (143)

Plate VIa Tintoretto (239)

Plate VIb Patenier (162)

Plate VIc Master of the St. Lucy Legend (147)

Plate VId Provoost (164)

Plate VIIa Memling (161)

Plate VIIb Van der Weyden (171)

Plate VIIc David (153)

Plate VIId Follower of Van der Goes (154)

Plate VIIIa Corneille de Lyon (183)

Plate VIIIb Holbein (211)

Plate VIIIc Greuze (190)

Plate VIIId Augustin (178)

of panel on which frame is carved: 11 × 8 in. (arched top.)

COLL: Count Ingenheim, Silesia; in 1925 with Knoedler, who acquired it from Drey of Munich with this provenance. Sold by Knoedler to Lord Bearsted in 1925.

EXH: Whitechapel, 1955, No. 84.

The Madonna, wearing a red robe, is seated on the ground before a low brick wall, holding the Child towards an angel who kneels at the left and offers Him an apple; beyond the garden wall is a valley with a wide river flowing round a castle and two Dominican monks walking along a path on the near bank. (This subject of the Madonna of Humility is probably Dominican in origin: cf. M. Meiss in *Art Bulletin*, XVIII, 1936, p. 457, note 52.)

When acquired by Knoedler the picture was ascribed to the School of Memlinc. The present attribution to the Master of the St. Catherine Legend is due to Dr. Friedländer (cf. Upton catalogue). Friedländer names the artist after the eponymous picture formerly in the collection of Baron van der Elst, Vienna (*Altniederländische Malerei*, vol. IV, No. 47, Pl. XLVI). For the possible identification of the Master with Pieter van der Weyden, cf. Friedländer, *op. cit.*, p. 108.

While No. 157 has much in common with the group of paintings collected by Friedländer under the name of this follower of Rogier van der Weyden, some doubts may be expressed as to whether the standard is high enough for the attribution to be accepted with certainty.

147 MASTER OF THE ST. LUCY LEGEND, active late fifteenth century

St. Jerome in a Landscape (*Plate VIc*)

Panel (Oak), 22⅛ × 15¾ in.

COLL: Carlo Ludovico di Borbone, Duke of Lucca (on the back of the panel is his crown and cypher, *C.L.*, surmounted by the number *73*). Not included in the Lucca sales held in London in 1840 and 1841 but at some period entered the collection of the Earls of Strathmore; at Streatlam Castle, Durham, and in all probability sold when the castle was demolished in the early 1920's. Acquired by Lord Bearsted by 1929.

LIT: Friedländer, 1937, vol. XIV, p. 105.

EXH: B.F.A.C., 1929, No. 31; Whitechapel, 1955, No. 74 (Pl. XXXI in catalogue); Musée

Communal, Bruges, *L'Art Flamand dans les Collections Britanniques*, 1956, No. 21 (Pl. 14 in catalogue).

The saint, wearing a soutane, kneels in the foreground looking up at a crucifix, right, his cardinal's cloak and hat placed beside him, the lion nearby. A river winds among wooded slopes to a lake surrounding a walled town, representing Bruges, in the distance. In the landscape are seen incidents from the life of the saint: on the right the merchants with their camels and the ass stolen from the monastery are chased by the lion, and on the left the ass is returned to the monastery.

The picture appears in the Upton catalogue under the authorship of Dirk Bouts, an attribution supported by Sir Martin Conway, who dates it *c.* 1450 (verbal opinion quoted in catalogue). It is given by Friedländer (*op. cit.*) to the Master of the St. Lucy Legend, and a statement made by Friedländer (July 1936) to the effect that the appearance of Bruges in the background is tantamount to the signature of the Master, is also quoted in the Upton catalogue.

The picture from which the Master takes his name is the *Legend of St. Lucy*, dated 1480, in the church of St. Jacques, Bruges. That the present picture can be dated subsequent to this is clear from the fact that the belfry of Bruges, represented in the background, is in its finished state. It was heightened between 1480 and 1490 and is shown in the St. Lucy altarpiece without the top storey and pointed roof (cf. Friedländer, vol. VI, p. 70). The Upton picture is therefore likely to have been painted *c.* 1490: the belfry was damaged by fire in 1493 and not rebuilt until 1499–1501, though this is not irrefutable evidence for dating the picture prior to 1493. The Church of Notre-Dame is also represented in the picture.

It should be pointed out that No. 147, reasonably associated with the Master of the St. Lucy Legend, stands out among his *œuvre* as being of particularly high quality.

158a MASTER OF THE ST. LUCY LEGEND, active late fifteenth century

St. John the Baptist

Panel (Oak), 32¾ × 10⅛ in.

COLL: Nos. 158a and b were with Douwes, Amsterdam, 1926; with Knoedler, 1928, from whom acquired by Lord Bearsted; alleged by Friedländer (1928) to have belonged to the

Duke of Norfolk, but this remains unconfirmed and the pictures were not included in the 1902 catalogue of the collection.

LIT: Friedländer, 1928, vol. VI, p. 140, No. 142; vol XIV, p. 104.

EXH: Whitechapel, 1955, No. 85 (Pl. XXX in catalogue).

COMPANION PICTURE: No. 158b. The present picture is probably the left wing of a triptych, or as joined here, a diptych, of which No. 158b is the corresponding panel.

St. John, wearing a purple robe over a hair shirt, stands on a rocky bank beside the Jordan, facing right and gesturing with his right hand; in the background he is seen baptizing Christ, an attendant angel on the bank beside him; in the distance a town on a flat plain.

158b MASTER OF THE ST. LUCY LEGEND, active late fifteenth century

St. Catherine of Alexandria

Panel (Oak), $32\frac{3}{4} \times 10\frac{1}{8}$ in.

COLL: as No. 158a.

LIT: as No. 158a.

EXH: as No. 158a.

RELATED PICTURE: a somewhat similar but slightly inferior picture, attributed to the Master of the St. Lucy Legend, is in the Johnson collection, Philadelphia (cf. W. R. Valentiner, *Catalogue*, 1913, vol II, No. 326, where it is mentioned that it resembles a picture of the subject in the museum at Pisa).

COMPANION PICTURE: No. 158a (cf. that picture).

St. Catherine, wearing a crown with fleur-de-lys, a blue-green dress and richly embroidered crimson and gold robes lined with ermine and studded with jewels, stands upon the pagan tyrant, Maximian II, by whose order she was beheaded; in her right hand she holds an open book from which she reads, with her left she supports a sword; in the background a winding path leads across flat country to a distant gatehouse.

It is possible that the Master, who frequently painted Bruges in the background of his pictures, is intending here to represent the Ostend Gate at Bruges. This gatehouse was reconstructed and its design altered in the early seventeenth century (cf. A. Duclos, *Bruges, Histoire et Souvenirs*, 1910, pp. 545–6), but its appearance prior to that date and subsequent

to 1433 (Duclos, p. 103) bears a superficial resemblance to the building here depicted.

159 MASTER OF THE MAGDALEN LEGEND, active late fifteenth and early sixteenth century

A young Man

Panel (Oak), $13\frac{1}{4} \times 9\frac{7}{8}$ in.

COLL: previous history and date of acquisition by Lord Bearsted unrecorded.

LIT: J. Tombu, 'Le Maître de la Legende de Marie-Madeleine', *Gazette des Beaux-Arts*, LXXI, 1929 (II), pp. 278, 280, repd.

EXH: Whitechapel, 1955, No. 82.

Half length, looking slightly left and downwards, wearing a grey dress embroidered with black floral designs and striped with gold, a white shirt with gold braid, a dark mauve velvet cloak and a black barette with a jewel decorated with the Virgin and Child; a circular pendant jewel with a design of the Annunciation is attached to a black ribbon round his neck; he holds a dagger and scabbard in both hands, with the initials *R. H.* engraved on the scabbard. Blue-green background.

The attribution to the Master of the Magdalen Legend is due to Hulin de Loo and Friedländer (cf. Upton catalogue, where the portrait is identified as Louis II of Hungary). This identification (from the letters *R. H.* on the dagger) is not confirmed by comparison with known engraved portraits of Louis, although the Master is credited with a portrait of the king's wife, Mary of Hungary (cf. Friedländer, vol. XII, p. 169, No. 34: dated c. 1528). Tombu (implied date of after 1520) agrees with the present attribution. For Hulin de Loo's equation of the Master of the Magdalen Legend with Bernaert van der Stockt, cf. Tombu, *op. cit.*, pp. 289–91, and for a further hypothesis concerning the identity of the master (Friedländer: as Pieter van Coninxloo), cf. No. 160.

160 Attributed to the MASTER OF THE MAGDALEN LEGEND, active late fifteenth and early sixteenth century

Philip the Fair

Panel (Oak), $16\frac{1}{2} \times 11\frac{1}{2}$ in.

COLL: C. H. Magniac sale, Christie's, 2 July 1892, lot 75, as Flemish School: bt. by

Donaldson; E. Steinkopf sale, Christie's, 24 May 1935, lot 73, as by Coninxloo: bt. by Martin for Lord Bearsted.

LIT: M. J. Onghena, *Iconografie van Philips de Schone*, 1952, pp. 82–3, No. 8, Pl. VIIa.

EXH: Whitechapel, 1955, No. 83.

RELATED PICTURES: Friedländer, 1926, vol. IV, p. 144, No. 83, gives a list of seven versions, four in private collections, others in Vienna, the Louvre and at Windsor. In vol. XII, p. 169, No. 32, he adds another, in 1934 with the London trade. For earlier portraits of Philip as a boy, cf. *ibid*, vol. XII, Nos. 30, 31, and vol. XIV, p. 127. A list of portraits is also given by Sánchez Cantón in *Catalogo de las Pinturas del Instituto de Valencia de Don Juan*, Madrid, 1923, pp. 10–12.

As a young man, nearly half length, facing half left, with fair hair to his shoulders, wearing a cloth of gold surcoat with dark fur collar and black barette, and order of the Golden Fleece.

Philip the Fair (1478–1506), Archduke of Austria, son of the Emperor Maximilian and Mary of Burgundy. He married Joan, second daughter of Ferdinand and Isabella of Castille, and was father of the Emperors Charles V and Ferdinand. In 1494 he was made governor of the Low Countries and in 1504 King of Castille and Leon and Philip I of Spain.

The original of this series of portraits of Philip le Beau (ex-Engel-Grosz, now Reinhart collection) was first attributed by Friedländer to the Master of the Joseph Legend (*op. cit.*, vol. IV); the others he suggests are workshop products, possibly by Jacob van Lathem, court painter to Philip. F. Winkler (article in Thieme-Becker, *Künstler-Lexikon*, 1928, vol. XXII, p. 418) attributes the series to Lathem. Friedländer later changed his attribution to the Master of the Magdalen Legend (*op cit.*, vol. XII), but in a note on p. 19 added that the Reinhart picture originated with the Master of St. Gilles. In 'Le Maître de St. Gilles', *Gazette des Beaux-Arts*, XVII, 1937, p. 222, No. 7, fig. 12, he gives this portrait to the artist of the title.

The present picture, not mentioned in any of the literature quoted above and formerly ascribed to Pieter van Coninxloo, Friedländer attributed to the Master of the Magdalen Legend in a verbal opinion given in 1936 (cf. Upton catalogue). For the possible identification of Coninxloo with the Master of the Magdalen Legend, cf. Friedländer, vol. XII,

pp. 21–24 and P. Wescher, 'Das Höfische Bildnis von Philipp dem Guten bis zu Karl V', *Pantheon*, XXVIII, 1941, p. 276. For further information on this series of portraits of Philip, including bibliography and a discussion of the identity of the sitter, cf. E. Michel, *Louvre Catalogue . . . Peintures Flamandes de XVe et XVIe Siècle*, Paris, 1953, pp. 103–5. The Louvre portrait of Philip (No. 2220b) is catalogued as School of Brussels, late fifteenth century, possibly from the Master of the Magdalen Legend *atelier*.

The date of this series of portraits of Philip is given by Friedländer (vol. XII, p. 169) as *c.* 1500. J. Tombu, 'Le Maître de la Legende de Marie-Madeleine', *Gazette des Beaux-Arts*, LXXI, 1929 (II), p. 284, mentions the Engel-Grosz (i.e. Reinhart) picture as probably having been painted prior to the Archduke's marriage (Philip married Joan the Mad in 1496) and those at Windsor and the Rijksmuseum (formerly in the collection of Lord Taunton) slightly earlier. The present picture which seems to be comparable with the Reinhart portrait in so far as the age of the sitter is concerned, can be considered superior to studio work. It is dated *c.* 1497–98 by Onghena.

161 HANS MEMLING, active 1485–1494

An unknown Man (*Plate VIIa*)

Panel (Oak), $6\frac{5}{8} \times 4\frac{3}{4}$ in. (arched top.)

COLL: with Colnaghi, 1921, then Knoedler from whom it was acquired by Lord Bearsted. The only history prior to this is the statement (Upton catalogue) that it came from a Russian collection. Knoedler's possess a letter from Dr. Friedländer (20.5.1922) giving the information that it was with de Burlet, a Berlin dealer, who found it in Vienna.

LIT: M. J. Friedländer, *Von Eyck bis Bruegel*, Berlin, 1921, p. 189 (listed under London: Colnaghi, Obach and Co.); *idem*, 'Zur Londoner Leihaustellung Belgischer Kunst', *Der Cicerone*, XIX, 1927, p. 212, Pl. 4; *idem*, 1928, vol VI, p. 131, No. 87, Pl. XLV; *idem*, 'Memling Exhibition at Bruges', *Burlington Magazine*, LXXV, 1939, p. 123.

EXH: B.F.A.C., 1924, No. 2; R.A., Winter, *Flemish and Belgian Art*, 1927, No. 50 (*Commemorative Catalogue*, No. 50, Pl. XXVIII); Musée Communal, Bruges, *Memling*, 1939, No. 41 (Pl. 20a in catalogue); Whitechapel, *Five Centuries of European Painting*, 1948,

No. 30; R.A., Winter, *Flemish Art*, 1953, No. 30; Whitechapel, 1955, No. 70 (Pl. XXXIII in catalogue).

A young man, head and shoulders, facing half left, with long dark hair, hands joined in prayer; he wears a brown cloak with a large fur collar over a black doublet with a white shirt visible at the neck; a ring on the index finger of the left hand.

This is likely to be the right wing of a diptych, the companion of which was a Madonna and Child. It was seen by Hulin de Loo who recorded his opinion in a letter to Knoedler's (17.8.1922) that it was a work by Memling.

162 JOACHIM PATENIER, active 1515–1524

The Temptation of Christ (*Plate VIb*)

Panel (Oak), $8\frac{1}{8} \times 8\frac{7}{8}$ in.

COLL: L. Rosenthal, 1934; his sale, Sotheby's, 29 April 1937, lot 119, repd.: bt. by Langton Douglas; date of acquisition by Lord Bearsted unrecorded.

EXH: Stern Gallery, Düsseldorf, 1934, No. 56 (Pl. 7 in catalogue); Whitechapel, 1955, No. 86 (Pl. XXVII in catalogue).

A rocky landscape with a river in the middle distance. On top of a grass-covered rock in the foreground stand Christ, wearing a blue robe, and the Devil, a bearded old man in a red cloak and hood. They are seen again on top of a precipitous rock towards the left.

'Certified by Dr. M. J. Friedländer as a very fine work by Joachim Patinir: in his opinion the figures are by another hand' (Upton catalogue). The date of this opinion is not quoted but since the picture does not appear in Friedländer's monograph on the artist in vol. IX of *Altniederländische Malerei*, nor among those listed in the addenda in vol. XIV (1937) it must be subsequent to that date. It was however exhibited as by Patenier in 1934.

The dichotomy between the figures and the landscape bears out Friedländer's opinion that, as in other works by Patenier, a second hand has added the figures.

163 FRANS POURBUS THE YOUNGER, 1569–1622

Martin Ruzé

Canvas, $25\frac{1}{2} \times 20\frac{3}{4}$ in.

SIGNED AND DATED: *AN. SAL. 1612. F.POURBUS. FE.*

INSCRIBED: *MESre. MARTIN RUZÉ CHEVALLIER Sr. DE BEAVLIEV CONSr. DV ROY. SECRE D'ESTAT ET GRAND TRESORIER DES ORDRES DE S. Mte. AGÉ DE 83. ANS*

COLL: said to have come from Saxham Hall, Suffolk (Upton catalogue); Col. E. G. Coles sale, Christie's, 19 November 1926, lot 28: bt. by F. Sabin who sold it to Lord Bearsted in 1927.

LIT: L. Burchard, article in Thieme-Becker, *Künstler-Lexikon*, 1933, vol. XXVII, p. 317.

EXH: R.A., Winter, *Flemish and Belgian Art*, 1927, No. 240 (*Commemorative Catalogue* No. 240); R.A., Winter, *17th Century Art in Europe*, 1938, No. 91; Whitechapel, *Five Centuries of European Painting*, 1948, No. 36; R.A., Winter, *Flemish Art*, 1953, No. 207; Whitechapel, 1955, No. 87; Musée Communal, Bruges, *L'Art Flamand dans les Collections Britanniques*, 1956, No. 58 (Pl. 44 in catalogue).

Nearly half length, body turned slightly right, head almost facing; he has a two-pointed beard and wears a brown doublet embroidered in black with spherical gold buttons set close together, a white linen ruff and the blue ribbon and order of the St. Esprit.

Ruzé first served Henry, Duke of Anjou, who as Henry III appointed him financial secretary and in 1588 secretary of state. Under Henry IV he was made grand treasurer of the orders of the king of France. In 1606 he relinquished the secretaryship of state, and dying childless in 1616 left his estates to Maréchal d'Effiat provided the latter adopted his name and arms.

164 JAN PROVOOST, active 1491–1529

The Virgin and St. Joseph at Bethlehem (*Plate VId*)

Panel (Oak), $34\frac{1}{2} \times 12\frac{1}{2}$ in.

COLL: Princess Villafranca y Salaparuta (of Palermo) sale, Christie's, 26 May 1922, lot 117: bt. by Knoedler, from whom it was acquired by Lord Bearsted. An unidentified seal on the back bears the initials *C. B.*

LIT: Friedländer, 1931, vol. IX, p. 151, No. 179.

EXH: R.A., Winter, *Flemish and Belgian Art*, 1927, No. 105 (*Commemorative Catalogue*, No. 105, Pl. XLIX); Knoedler, London, *Masterpieces through four Centuries*, 1935, No. 14 (1); Whitechapel, 1955, No. 76.

The Virgin stands facing right, wearing a white headdress and blue mantle over a mauve robe; facing her is St. Joseph, a basket over his left shoulder, a rope in his right hand tethering an ass, the head of which is seen low right. In the centre a woman holds a small child in her arms, and in the background is a red brick house and a view of a street leading to a church.

Verso: the *grisaille* figure of the Virgin Annunciate stands in a niche, facing half right and wearing flowing robes, a book in her right hand held against her body, her left hand held forward; at the left, a vase of lilies.

The episode of the journey from Nazareth to Bethlehem is rarely depicted (according to L. Réau, *Iconographie de L'Art Chrétien*, 1957, vol. II (2), p. 216, it may have been eliminated through confusion with the *Flight into Egypt*). The scene illustrated shows the arrival of Mary and Joseph in Bethlehem where they were summoned to pay tax before the birth of Christ (Luke ii. 1–5).

The compositions on both sides of the panel are evidence that this is the left wing of an altarpiece, probably a triptych. When the shutters were closed the Angel of the Annunciation would therefore be seen to appear from the right, a departure from the usual iconography, but adopted by Provoost on other occasions.

It is recorded in the Upton catalogue that the picture was accepted by Hulin de Loo in 1920 as unquestionably by Provoost. It would appear to be a work of the (?) early 1520s in which a tendency towards Antwerp mannerism combines with the tradition of the school of Bruges, where the artist had settled in 1494.

165 JAN PROVOOST, active 1491–1529

The Nativity at Night

Panel (Oak), 28 × 12¼ in.

COLL: anonymous sale, Christie's, 12 December 1924, lot 116 (as by van der Goes), the owner divulged in the Upton catalogue as Elizabeth, Countess of Northesk. It was bought by F. Sabin, who sold it to Lord Bearsted in 1927. An indistinct seal is on the back of the panel.

LIT: Friedländer, 1931, vol. IX, pp. 92, 147, No. 142, Pl. LXXI; D. Sutton, 'Flemish Painting at the Royal Academy', *Les Arts Plastiques*, VI, 1954, p. 23, fig. 19.

EXH: B.F.A.C., 1927, No. 7; Knoedler, London, *Masterpieces through four Centuries*,

1935, No. 14 (II); Whitechapel, *Five Centuries of European Painting*, 1948, No. 38; R.A., Winter, *Flemish Art*, 1953, No. 34; Antwerp, Gallery of Fine Art, *The Madonna in Art*, 1955, No. 83; Whitechapel, 1955, No. 77.

The interior of a ruined brick building with the Virgin kneeling, surrounded by child angels, adoring the Child who lies on the ground before her; she wears a pale blue-grey robe and hood and dark blue mantle. In the background St. Joseph, carrying a lantern, stands beside a woman who may be one of the two midwives in attendance at the birth of Christ; in the foreground the ox and ass lie on either side of the Child and at the right two shepherds peer through a window. Light radiates from the Child and illuminates the face of the Madonna and part of her robe.

Probably the left wing of a triptych. G. Ring ('Additions to the Work of Jan Provost . . .' *Burlington Magazine*, LXXIX, 1941, p. 159), describing a daylight *Nativity* by Provoost (one of a series of scenes from the Life of the Virgin which can be dated before *c.* 1495) observes that the Child is not represented diffusing light as in the later version of the subject in Lord Bearsted's collection.

According to the Upton catalogue the picture was certified by Dr. Friedländer in 1905. The further information that it was included in Friedländer's *Von Eyck bis Bruegel* (1921, p. 196) is mistaken, the only listed picture by Provoost of this subject being a *Birth of Christ* in the possession of an Amsterdam dealer in 1920. This is probably Friedländer, *Altniederländische Malerei*, vol. IX, No. 143 (with Goudstikker).

For a note on Nativities at Night, with the Child lying on the ground, cf. Martin Davies, *National Gallery Catalogue: Early Netherlandish School*, 1945, p. 38, No. 2159 (Follower of van der Goes). The example by Sittow at Upton (No. 167) shows the Child lying in a crib.

166 Imitator of SIR PETER PAUL RUBENS, 1577–1640

Judas Maccabaeus praying for the Dead

Panel (concealed by canvas backing), 25⅛ × 19½ in.

COLL: bought privately by Lord Bearsted in 1936 from Capt. A. Cunningham Graham; previous history untraced.

EXH: Brussels, Musée des Beaux-Arts, *Esquisses de Rubens*, 1937, No. 5 (Pl. 1 in catalogue); Whitechapel, 1955, No. 90.

RELATED PICTURE: see below.

In the background a victory procession passes to the left. Judas Maccabaeus, wearing armour and a red cloak, stands on a mound in the centre, apparently praying, while a priest summons him to join the procession. In the foreground the idols are found on the dead and a Jew hands a gold object to a priest.

The incident depicted is taken from II Maccabees xii. 39–42. On the day after the Sabbath following their victory over the men of Gorgias the Jews go to bury their dead and pray for them. They realize the cause of their comrades' deaths when they discover on their corpses the idols of the Jamnites, forbidden to the Jews, and 'all men therefore praising the Lord . . . betook themselves unto prayer'.

Rubens's interpretation gives the impression of an event more immediately connected with the battle, and shows a victory procession and Judas alone about to offer prayers for the slain.

Hitherto catalogued and exhibited as by Rubens. While this (?)seventeenth-century sketch is not an exact copy of the picture in Nantes (cf. *infra*), its quality is such that it cannot be accepted as being by Rubens. The difference in detail between it and the Nantes altarpiece would, according to Michael Jaffé, be most plausibly explained by it being a copy of a lost *modello*, a reasonable possibility in view of the fact that Rubens's sketches were copied from an early date and even during his own lifetime.

The altarpiece to which No. 166 is related was commissioned by Maximilien Vilain, Bishop of Tournai from 1615–44, for the altar of the Souls of Purgatory in Tournai Cathedral, of which Rubens's *Purgatory* formed the front and the *Judas Maccabaeus*, a prefiguration of the Resurrection, the back. In 1795 the complete altarpiece was removed by the French Republic. The *Purgatory* was returned in 1815 and was later replaced in the cathedral, but the *Judas Maccabaeus* was retained and is now in the museum at Nantes.

The altarpiece has been differently dated: A. Rosenberg, *Rubens (Klassiker der Kunst)*, 1905, p. 192: *c.* 1618–20; M. Rooses, *Bulletin Rubens*, V, Antwerp 1910, p. 286, No. 137: *c.* 1618; R. Oldenberg, *Rubens (Klassiker der Kunst)*, 1921, p. 353: *c.* 1635. Mr. Jaffé judges the latter date to be correct.

The present sketch was dated *c.* 1630 in the catalogue of the 1937 Brussels exhibition.

167 MICHAEL SITTOW, 1469–1525

The Nativity at Night

Panel (Oak), 15 × 11⅞ in.

COLL: owned by Lord Bearsted in 1934; previously with the Bachstitz Gallery, The Hague, but included in the 1935 *Bulletin* of this gallery, where it was said to have come from a Spanish collection. In the intermediate period (1931) it was with Blumenreich, Berlin.

LIT: F. Winkler, 'Master Michel', *Art in America*, XIX, 1931, p. 257, fig. 8; E. P. Richardson, 'Three Paintings by Master Michel', *Art Quarterly*, II, 1939, p. 104; P. Johansen, 'Master Michel Sittow', *Jahrbuch der Preuszischen Kunstsammlungen*, LXI, 1940, p. 35, catalogue No. 3; article by M. J. Friedländer in *Bulletin of Bachstitz Gallery*, The Hague, 1935, pp. 27–28, repd.; F. Davis, *Illustrated London News*, CLXXXVI, 1935, p. 70, repd.; X. de Salas, *Goya*, VI, 1955, p. 365, and in *Archivo Español de Arte*, 112 1955, p. 359 (No. 52), Pl. VI.

EXH: B.F.A.C., 1934, No. 27; Whitechapel, 1955, No. 80.

The Virgin kneels at the left of the Child who lies in a crib in the centre; opposite her, surrounding the cradle, are four angels praying, while three others hover above; in the background the ox and ass, and to the left, St. Joseph. Light streams from the Child, but the greater part of the composition is left in shadow.

Catalogued by Johansen and referred to by Friedländer as being by Sittow. Winkler includes it 'tentatively in the circle of the works by Master Michiel'. Richardson (fig. 1) publishes an altarpiece (size 48 × 29 in.), now in the Philadelphia Museum (Wilsbach collection), which he suggests is by Sittow (catalogued as by David) and which has affinities with the present picture.

For a note on *Nativities at Night*, with the Child in the crib, cf. Martin Davies, *National Gallery Catalogue: Early Netherlandish School*, 1945, p. 37, No. 4081 (attributed to Geertgen). The example by Provoost at Upton (No. 165) shows the Child lying on the ground.

168 SON, JORIS VAN

This picture, included in the 1950 catalogue, is the property of Lord Bearsted and is therefore omitted from the present edition.

69 Studio of SIR ANTHONY VAN DYCK,
1599–1641

Queen Henrietta Maria

Canvas, 74 × 45½ in.

COLL: Duke of Osuna (according to 1892 sale catalogue); Murrieta sale, Christie's, 14 May 1892, lot 123: bt. by M. Colnaghi; date of acquisition by Lord Bearsted unrecorded.

RELATED PICTURE: a similar portrait is in Castello Sforza, Milan (cf. E. Jacobsen, 'La Galleria de Castello Sforzesco', *L'Arte*, IV, 1901, p. 309, repd., where it is listed as probably by Van Dyck with studio assistance). Oliver Millar, in the catalogue of the Flemish Exhibition at the Royal Academy, 1953, No. 160 (*The Great Piece*), remarks on the affinity of the type of portrait of the Queen in this group to the standing full length in Milan.

Full length, standing slightly right on a carpet, head turned to the left, wearing a gold coloured satin dress with white lace collar and cuffs, her left hand resting on a table covered with a blue-green cloth on which is her crown, her right hand at her waist.

1609–69. Youngest daughter of Henry IV and Marie de' Medici; Queen Consort of Charles I, whom she married in 1625.

---

70 Studio of SIR ANTHONY VAN DYCK,
1599–1641

Margaret of Lorraine

Canvas, 73½ × 45¾ in.

COLL: as No. 169 (lot 122 in Murrieta sale).

INSCRIBED (indistinctly): *A VAN DYCK F Ao 1632*

RELATED PICTURES: (I) A similar portrait is illustrated by Glück (*Van Dyck, Klassiker der Kunst*, 1931, p. 432) in the collection of Prince Yussopoff. Glück writes that the composition of this portrait, if not the entire execution, is authenticated by a study in the British Museum (cf. A. M. Hind, *Dutch and Flemish Drawings in the British Museum*, 1923, vol. II, p. 63, No. 38, Pl. XXX). (II) A good studio version from the Orléans collection, similar except that the sitter holds a fan in her left hand, is at Woburn (cf. Scharf, *Catalogue*, 1890, No. 154).

An engraving of the head and shoulders in reverse by S. A. Bolswert, with slight variations, is included in Van Dyck's *Iconography* (No. 23). The study for this is at Munich.

Full length, standing to right in an apartment, head turned towards the spectator, left hand resting on a table, right by her side; she wears a white satin dress richly embroidered with silver braid, large white sleeves and pink bows, white lace collar and cuffs and a loose black coat.

Margaret (1613–72), daughter of Francis, Count of Vaudemont, and sister of Charles, 3rd Duke of Lorraine, married Gaston d'Orléans, younger son of Henry IV and Marie de' Medici, in 1632.

The picture was formerly catalogued as 'Comtesse de la Croix', and the related pen and sepia drawing (which appears to be of uncertain authenticity) was tentatively associated by Hind (*op. cit.*) with Maria Clara de Croy. The Yussopoff portrait was described by Glück as an unknown lady and only the Woburn version was catalogued as a portrait of Margaret of Lorraine (cf. Scharf, *op. cit.*).

There can be no doubt that the latter identification, which is confirmed by Bolswert's engraving, is correct, and this is further borne out by comparison with Van Dyck's portrait of this sitter, dated 1634, in the Uffizi. It is doubtful whether much reliance can be placed on the inscribed date of 1632. It was not until 1634–35, when he was in Flanders, that Van Dyck painted the series of Orléans portraits.

---

171 ROGIER VAN DER WEYDEN,
c. 1399–1464

An unknown Man (*Plate VIIb*)

Panel (Oak), 7⅞ × 6 in.

COLL: no history known before 1920 when it was bought by Knoedler, together with Parrish Watson of New York, from the executors of the Bulwer family, Norfolk (of Heydon Hall?). Shortly afterwards it was acquired by Lord Bearsted. It has however been confused with the *Portrait of a Monk* formerly attributed to Rogier van der Weyden, which was lot 146 in the John Linnell sale, Christie's, 15 March 1918, and is now in the Metropolitan Museum, New York (Dreicer Bequest) as Hugo van der Goes. The Upton portrait, which was never in the Dreicer collection except when sent for a period on approval by Knoedler, was described by Friedländer (*Von Eyck bis Bruegel*) as belonging to Dreicer, 'ex-Bulver collection'; while in *Art in America*, in Friedländer's article on the present picture (which he had seen in London in 1914) the accompanying reproduction showed the Dreicer portrait. Friedländer corrected the false Dreicer provenance in

Altniederländische Malerei, but before that it had been referred to by Conway (see *infra*) as being in the Dreicer collection, and tentatively by Hulin de Loo who also stated that it had been shown to him by More Adey before 1914, when it was in the possession of a friend who had brought it from Canada. The hypothesis that it belonged to Charles Butler was probably caused through confusion with the name of Bulwer.

LIT: Sir Martin Conway, *The Van Eycks and their Followers*, London, 1921, p. 148, Pl. V, fig. 4; M. J. Friedländer, *Von Eyck bis Bruegel*, Berlin, 1921, p. 185, *idem*, *Art in America*, IX, 1921, p. 188 (wrong picture repd.: see above under Coll.); Hulin de Loo, 'Diptychs by Rogier van der Weyden (1)', *Burlington Magazine*, XLIII, 1923, p. 54; Friedländer, 1924, vol. II, pp. 41, 106, No. 45, Pl. XXXVIII; *idem*, 'Zur Londoner Leihaustellung Belgischer Kunst', *Der Cicerone*, XIX, 1927, p. 208, Pl. 3; J. Destrée, *Roger de la Pasture van der Weyden*, Paris, 1930, vol, I, p. 201, No. 135; vol. II, Pl. 135; H. Dimier, 'Chronique sur l'art des Pays-Bas en France', *Oud Holland*, LIII, 1936, p. 50, fig. 5; V. Bloch, 'From Van Eyck to Brueghel', *Burlington Magazine*, LXVIII, 1936, p. 95, repd., p. 94b; W. Schöne, *Dieric Bouts und seine Schule*, Berlin, 1938, p. 62, No. 30; F. Winkler, article in Thieme-Becker, *Künstler-Lexikon*, 1942, vol. XXXV, p. 475; H. Beenken, *Rogier van der Weyden*, Munich, 1951, p. 71, Pl. 36; E. Panofsky, *Early Netherlandish Painting*, Cambridge, Mass., 1953, pp. 294, 497; F. Grossmann, 'Flemish Painting at Bruges', *Burlington Magazine*, XCIX, 1957, p. 4.

EXH: B.F.A.C., 1924, No. 6; R.A., Winter, *Flemish and Belgian Art*, 1927, No. 46 (*Commemorative Catalogue*, No. 46, Pl. XXV); Brussels, *Exposition Internationale, Cinq Siècles d'Art*, 1935, No. 12; Paris, Musée de l'Orangerie, *De Van Eyck à Bruegel*, 1935, No. 96; Whitechapel, *Five Centuries of European Painting*, 1948, No. 70; R.A., Winter, *Flemish Art*, 1953, No. 31; Whitechapel, 1955, No. 69; Musée Communal, Bruges, *L'Art Flamand dans les Collections Britanniques*, 1956, No. 5 (Pl. 5 in catalogue).

A young man, head and shoulders, facing half left, wearing a dark dress with plain collar, his hands joined in prayer, a ring on the little finger of the left hand. Turquoise background. On the back of the panel is a later inscription, *R. Hen VI.*

Probably the right wing of a diptych, of which the corresponding panel would have been the *Madonna and Child*; accepted by Friedländer and others as an autograph work, but only attributed to Rogier by Destrée.

Dated *c.* 1460 by Friedländer (*Altniederländische Malerei*), Beenken and Panofsky, and in Schöne's chronological list, *c.* 1454–59. Hulin de Loo remarks that the long hair style belongs to the later sixties and that unless the sitter was a foreigner, which seems unlikely, the portrait must have been painted at the end of the artist's life. Panofsky (p. 497, note 14) puts forward the theory that it may be a fragment: 'The picture is however so small (19 × 14 cm. only about half the usual size)'—i.e. of analogous devotional portraits: cf. H. de Loo, *Burlington Magazine*, XLIII, 1923, pp. 53f, and XLIV, 1924, pp. 179f—'that it may be worthwhile to investigate whether it is a portrait cut from a larger composition rather than the wing of a devotional diptych.' Grossmann remarks that the blue ground 'does not inspire too much confidence and may hide a part of the original composition'.

The painted surface only reaches to the edge of the unbevelled panel at the bottom; at the top and sides it stops ⅛ in. short of the edge of the panel and has therefore not been cut at these three sides. The picture has not been X-ray photographed.

145 Follower of ROGIER VAN DER WEYDEN, *c.* 1399–1464

Christ and St. John the Baptist

Panel (Oak), 25¾ × 16⅝ in.

Later inscription with indistinct Dutch text (Matthew, iii, 14–15).

COLL: previous history unrecorded, but acquired by Lord Bearsted by 1924.

LIT: Friedländer, 1924, vol. II, p. 120, No. 86, Pl. LXIX; F. Winkler, article in Thieme-Becker, *Künstler-Lexikon*, 1937, vol. XXXV, p. 475.

EXH: Whitechapel, 1955, No. 72.

COMPANION PICTURE: No. 146. The present picture is probably the right wing of an altarpiece of which No. 146 is the corresponding panel.

Our Lord stands left in an extensive undulating landscape by the river Jordan, wearing a blue mantle; He looks down at St. John, in red

Plate IXb El Greco (255)

Plate IXa Fouquet (184)

Plate Xa Domenico Tiepolo (238)

Plate Xb Follower of Verrocchio (225)

Plate Xc Attributed to Pacher (212)

Plate Xd Lotto (235)

robes over a hair shirt, kneeling at His feet. The incident is explained by the text inscribed (in Dutch) above St. John ('I have need to be baptized of thee, and comest thou to me?') and above Jesus ('Suffer it to be so now: for thus it becometh us to fulfil all righteousness').

In the Upton catalogue as by Dirk Bouts, but listed by Friedländer as a picture of 'ungewöhnlich Einfachkeit und Würde' by a close follower of Rogier van der Weyden, and included by Winkler as by a (?)Follower.

146 Follower of ROGIER VAN DER WEYDEN, c. 1399–1464

The Calling of Andrew and Simon Peter

Panel (Oak), $26\frac{3}{4} \times 16\frac{5}{8}$ in.

Formerly inscribed with text in Dutch, now illegible.

COLL: as No. 145.

LIT: as No. 145 (not repd. by Friedländer).

EXH: Whitechapel, 1955, No. 73.

COMPANION PICTURE: No. 145 (cf. that picture).

The first two disciples stand, left, behind Christ, who wears a blue robe. He turns towards them and points to the entrance of his dwelling within the doorway of which the Virgin Mary is seated, sewing.

The picture, which is probably the left wing of an altarpiece, was formerly entitled *Christ in the House of Martha*, but the textual source is more likely to be St. John i, 37–39, where the two disciples of John followed Jesus, 'came and saw where he dwelt, and abode with him that day'.

For attribution cf. No. 145.

152 JOACHIM WTEWAEL, 1588–1638

Diana and Actaeon

Panel (Oak), $11\frac{1}{4} \times 15\frac{1}{2}$ in.

COLL: previous history and date of acquisition by Lord Bearsted unrecorded.

Diana and her nymphs in the foreground are surprised by Actaeon approaching from an avenue behind them; right, a valley with a stream and cottages, and a wooded hill beyond.

Hitherto catalogued as by Gillis van Coninxloo, but almost certainly by Wtewael whose style it closely resembles. The form of composition with Actaeon appearing between the trees in the background is exactly paralleled in a panel of 1607 in the Kunsthistorisches Museum, Vienna (cf. C. Lindemann, *Wtewael*, 1929, p. 251, No. VIII, Pl. V), for which there is a drawing in Darmstadt, and by a small painting on copper which was in the Doetsch sale, London, 1895 (Lindemann, No. XXVIII, Pl. V). In both of these the figure of Actaeon is practically identical to the counterpart in No. 152, and the seated nymphs on either side of the right-hand group in the present picture repeat corresponding figures in the Doetsch and Vienna pictures. The other compositions are centralized round the figure of Actaeon and No. 152 is alone in having the extended landscape.

172, 173 (*Style of Jan Brueghel*) are to be found preceding No. 150 (*Jan Brueghel the Younger*)

The French School

178 JEAN-BAPTISTE-JACQUES AUGUSTIN, 1759–1832

The Artist's Mother (*Plate VIIId*)

Black chalk heightened with white, $7\frac{1}{4} \times 5\frac{5}{8}$ in. (oval).

DATED: *1793* (in pencil).

INSCRIBED in ink on reverse: *Madame Augustin Mère dessinée Par son fils à St. Dié en Lorraine en 1791, et fini à Paris en 1793*

COLL: Pierpont Morgan sale, Christie's, 27 June 1935, lot 728: bt. by Martin for Lord Bearsted.

LIT: G. C. Williamson, *Catalogue of Collection of Miniatures of Pierpont Morgan*, London, 1908, vol. IV, No. 678, Pl. CCXLIV.

Head and shoulders, profile to left, wearing fur-trimmed mantle and headdress ornamented with lace and ribbons.

The sitter is Marie-Françoise Guillaume, wife of Nicolas Augustin, the parents of J. B. Augustin. Two other portraits of her by her son (Williamson, Nos. 668, 738) were among the large collection of works by this artist owned by Pierpont Morgan.

179 FRANÇOIS BOUCHER, 1703–1770

Venus and Vulcan

Papier mâché (square of 1 in. at bottom left-hand corner a replacement), $14\frac{5}{8} \times 21\frac{5}{8}$ in.

COLL: previous history and date of acquisition by Lord Bearsted unrecorded.

EXH: Whitechapel, *Five Centuries of European Painting*, 1948, No. 6.

RELATED PICTURE: No. 179 is a sketch for the picture in the Louvre (La Caze, 161), which is signed and dated 1747 (cf. A. Michel, *François Boucher*, Paris, 1907, p. 22, No. 347). The composition of the sketch corresponds with the finished picture, but the latter is an oval. Also related is an oval *grisaille* sketch in the Louvre (La Caze, 164).

Vulcan is seated on a red cloak in the centre, holding a sword and hammer; he looks over his left shoulder to Venus, who stands behind him; in front of her Cupid is seated with a dove by an anvil; right, two youths hold up to Vulcan a helmet and cuirass; in the left background two smiths at a forge.

180 Atelier of FRANÇOIS CLOUET, c. 1510–1572

Francis I of France on Horseback

Panel (Oak), $10\frac{3}{4} \times 8\frac{3}{4}$ in.

COLL: C. H. Magniac sale, Christie's, 2 July 1892, lot 86, as attributed to Jean Clouet: bt. by Durlacher; E. Steinkopf sale, Christie's, 24 May 1935, lot 71, as by Jean Clouet: bt. by Martin for Lord Bearsted.

LIT: L. Dimier, *Le Portrait du XVIe Siècle*, Paris, 1904, p. 14.

EXH: Society of Arts, London, *Ancient and Medieval Art*, 1850, No. 785; B.F.A.C., 1937, No. 64 (as by François Clouet); Whitechapel, 1955, No. 43 (Pl. XVI in catalogue).

RELATED PICTURES: (I) Uffizi, No. 667 (panel, $10\frac{5}{8} \times 8\frac{5}{8}$ in.): with differences that the king wears a cap and the columns are not fluted (repd. by Dimier, *Histoire de la Peinture de Portrait en France*, Paris, 1924, vol. I, Pl. 8). (II) Mme Philipson collection, Brussels: a similar portrait (panel, $11 \times 9\frac{1}{2}$ in.) to that in the Louvre (see below). It was exhibited at Ghent, *Charles V and his Time*, 1955, No. 22 (repd. in catalogue where it is described as *Atelier* of François Clouet). The pose of the horse, probably deriving from the statue of Marcus Aurelius, is repeated in the large equestrian portrait of Henri II in the Metropolitan Museum, New York.

RELATED DRAWINGS: (I) Louvre, No. 683 (gouache on vellum, $12\frac{5}{8} \times 10\frac{1}{4}$ in.): with differences that the king wears a cap and there is neither architecture nor landscape (repd. by Moreau-Nélaton, *Les Clouet et leurs Emules*, Paris, 1924, vol. II, fig. 455). (II) Crayon copy at Chantilly, No. 146 (Dimier, *Portrait en*

France, 1924, vol. I, No. 129). (III) Crayon copy in the Hermitage (*Catalogue des Estampes*, No. 25; Dimier, *op. cit.*, No. 130). The same horse occurs in two drawings at Chantilly of Henry II (Nos. 334, 396; Dimier, *op. cit.*, Nos. 1307, 1309) and one of Charles IX (No. 405; Dimier, *op. cit.*, No. 1318).

COMPANION PICTURE: No. 181.

The king, bareheaded, head turned towards the spectator, rides to the left, mounted on a white horse with black fetlocks, mane and tail; he wears a suit of black armour damascened with silver and carries a gilt mace in his right hand; the saddle and harness of the horse are crimson and gold, and yellow, pink and black ostrich feathers are carried at its poll; to the right is a gateway or triumphal arch with fluted columns, partly visible. The horizon, low in the picture, is bounded by bare hills.

Francis I (1495–1547) succeeded his cousin, Louis XII, whose daughter he had married, in 1515. He appointed François Clouet court painter in 1541 on the death of the artist's father Jean, whose name had appeared in the royal accounts from 1515 onwards.

Previously attributed to Jean Clouet (Upton catalogue). Beyond a mention in Dimier that the 'Steinkopf' picture is a copy of the Uffizi portrait, it appears that no literature refers to the present picture. Its quality entitles it to be regarded as close to an autograph work, or as a very good studio version, but the difficulty of determining whether it should be associated with Jean or François Clouet can be understood from a selection of references to the two important works to which it is related.

1. L. de Laborde, *La Renaissance des Arts à la Cour de France*, Paris, 1850, vol. I, p. 18: Uffizi portrait by Jean (it was formerly catalogued as Holbein) and the Louvre portrait (then Sauvageot collection) as a repetition.

2. L. Dimier, *French Painting in the 16th Century*, London, 1904, pp. 124–5: Uffizi and Louvre portraits both after a lost original, probably on a large scale, by François. They cannot be by Jean since Francis I is depicted as being about fifty, i.e. at a date subsequent to Jean's death. (In this context it does not seem possible to form any judgement of the king's age in the present portrait.)

3. L. Dimier, *Le Portrait du XVIe Siècle*, Paris, 1904, p. 14: Uffizi picture by Jean on corrected estimation of king's age. Louvre version is a repetition (p. 13).

4. A. Germain, *Les Clouet*, Paris, 1906, pp. 55–56: by François, but both Louvre and Uffizi portraits may be repetitions. Date, 1541–45.

5. E. Moreau-Nélaton, *Les Clouet*, Paris, 1908, p. 14: Uffizi and Louvre portraits attributed to François.

6. L. Dimier, article in Thieme-Becker, *Künstler-Lexikon*, 1912, vol. VII, p. 120: Uffizi portrait attributed to Jean.

7. H. S. Ede, 'Authenticated Information concerning J. and F. Clouet', *Burlington Magazine*, XLII, 1923, p. 117: Uffizi picture and Louvre 'copy' ascribed to François.

8. L. Dimier, *Histoire de la Peinture de Portrait en France*, Paris, 1925, vol. II, p. 34, No. 145: Uffizi portrait catalogued as *Le Présumé Jean Clouet*, c. 1540, and Louvre (p. 132, No. 535) as by François.

9. C. Maumené and L. d'Harcourt, *Iconographie des Rois de France*, 1928, pp. 127–8, Nos. 27a, 29: attributed to Jean.

10. I. Adler, 'Die Clouet', *Jahrbuch der Kunsthistorischen Sammlungen in Wien*, N.F.III, 1929, p. 242: Uffizi picture by Jean.

11. R.A., *French Art*, 1932, No. 87: Uffizi portrait exhibited as by François; the Louvre referred to as a copy, perhaps from the workshop of François.

12. Uffizi, *Catalogue*, 1953: portrait listed as by François.

In view of the foregoing it seems superfluous to offer an attribution for the present picture, but as its companion (No. 181) can be more plausibly connected with François than with Jean Clouet, the former attribution is adopted here.

181 Atelier of FRANÇOIS CLOUET, *c. 1510–1572*

Henry II of France on Horseback

Panel (Oak), $10\frac{5}{8} \times 8\frac{3}{4}$ in.

COLL: William II of Holland sale, New Palace, Amsterdam, 12 August 1850, lot 99, as portrait of Don John of Austria; C. H. Magniac sale, Christie's, 2 July 1892, lot 87, as attributed to Jean Clouet: bt. by Durlacher; E. Steinkopf sale, Christie's, 24 May 1935, lot 72, as by Jean Clouet: bt. by Martin for Lord Bearsted.

LIT: C. J. Nieuwenhuys, *Description . . . des Tableaux de S. M. le Roi des Pays-Bas*, Brussels, 1843, No. 99; L. de Laborde, *La Renaissance des Arts à la Cour de France*,

Paris, 1850, vol. I, pp. 148–9; and *Additions . . .*, 1855, pp. 574–7; L. Dimier, *Le Portrait du XVIe Siècle*, Paris, 1904, p. 15; Sir James Mann, 'A Parade Armour of Henri II', *Country Life*, LXXXIII, 1938, p. 603.

EXH: B.F.A.C., 1937, No. 65 (as by François Clouet); Whitechapel, 1955, No. 44.

RELATED DRAWINGS: (I) The head of the king is very close to a pencil portrait, profile to left, at Chantilly (No. 248): cf. Dimier, *Histoire de la Peinture de Portrait en France*, Paris, 1925, vol. II, p. 88, No. 344, as Anonymous Master of 1550 (repd., vol. I, Pl. 15, bottom right), dated *c.* 1547. (II) The composition is similar to a red and black chalk drawing (in reverse) at Chantilly (No. 334: Dimier, *Portrait en France*, vol. II, p. 325, No. 1307) in which the king wears a cap and in which the horse is the same as in the portraits of Francis I (cf. No. 180). Unlike the present picture there are no distant hills visible in this drawing, but it should be noted that the drawing has suffered some rubbing and the background hills in No. 181 have been overpainted.

COMPANION PICTURE: No. 180.

The king, bareheaded, in profile, mounted on a black horse, rides to the left; he wears black armour damascened with silver and carries a gilt mace in his right hand; the harness of the horse is white with gold braiding and studs, and white and green ostrich feathers adorn its poll; to the left, part of a building or gateway is visible; low horizon.

Henry II (1519–59), second son of Francis I, whom he succeeded to the French throne in 1547; in 1553 he married Catherine de' Medici.

The picture was previously attributed to Jean Clouet (Upton catalogue). It was catalogued by Nieuwenhuys as a portrait of Don John of Austria by François Clouet. Laborde (*op. cit.*, 1850) first accepted it as by Jean Clouet and believed it to represent Henry II, aged 29 in 1546, and to have been painted as a pendant to the Francis I now in the Uffizi (cf. No. 180), to which picture he considered it inferior. He later (*op. cit.*, 1855) regarded it as a small repetition of a large equestrian portrait painted by François for Henry II's coronation in 1547, the existence of which was inferred from a passage in Etienne Jodelle's *Recueil des Inscriptions, Devises, Figures et Masquerades ordonnées en l'Hostel de Ville à Paris le Jeudi 17 Fevrier, 1558*, describing a picture in the following terms: *icon Henrici equitantis domi sic super Janetio pictore Parisiensi excellentissimo in majore tabula depincti*. The words *equitantis domi* suggest that the king was not wearing armour. Dimier (*French Painting in the 16th Century*, London, 1904, p. 138) thought that the prototype for the portrait might be recognized in a version formerly at Azy-le-Rideau (exh: Paris, *Primitifs Français*, 1904, No. 188, as by François Clouet). This portrait, which is now in the Metropolitan Museum, New York, shows the king riding to the left, wearing a cap and without armour.

Dimier (*Le Portrait du XVIe Siècle*, 1904, pp. 14–15) referring to No. 376 in the *Primitifs Français* exhibition—an equestrian portrait in profile of the Dauphin François, son of Henry II (Gustave de Rothschild collection)—states that it was probably painted late in the sixteenth century and belongs to a series of Valois princes at Chantilly (where No. 280 is a repetition of the Rothschild picture) which should be distinguished from the 'Steinkopf' (i.e. Upton) picture; the latter, like the Louvre and Uffizi portraits of Francis I, being of superior quality and having been painted fifty years earlier. (These gouaches of Valois princes referred to by Dimier are inferior indeed and their quality can in no way bear comparison with the Upton portrait.)

Sir James Mann points out that the armour worn by the king is identical to a suit in the Astor collection at Hever Castle, which he believes to be from the Negroli *Atelier*.

Like the preceding picture, No. 181 must be left with an indefinite attribution, but as Henry was only twenty-two when Jean Clouet died and appears to be older than this in the present picture, it seems reasonable to associate it with François.

180, 181 CLOUET, JEAN (Attributed to)
See *Clouet, François (Atelier of)*

182 Style of CORNEILLE DE LYON,
active 1533/54–1574

An unknown Man

Panel (Lime), $6 \times 4\frac{7}{8}$ in. (oval).

INSCRIBED (indistinctly): *So . . . Bernadini.*

COLL: previous history and date of acquisition by Lord Bearsted unrecorded.

EXH: Whitechapel, 1955, No. 45.

Head and shoulders, bearded, turned slightly to right, wearing a black coat with white collar just perceptible and black cap. Green background. An old inscription on the back of the panel states that the portrait represents Pier Luigi Farnese, Duke of Parma and Piacenza, by Holbein.

For attributions to Corneille de Lyon, see No. 183.

183 Style of CORNEILLE DE LYON, active 1533/34–1574

An unknown Man (*Plate VIIIa*)

Panel (Oak), diam. 5 in. (circular).

COLL: Huldschinsky sale, Berlin, 10 May 1928, lot 62, repd.; M. L. Schiff sale, Christie's, 24 June 1938, lot 64, repd.: bt. by Martin for Lord Bearsted.

EXH: Whitechapel, 1955, No. 46.

Head and shoulders, bearded and with slight moustache, almost facing; he wears a black coat with salmon-pink lining visible at the neck, white shirt and black cap. Dark-green background.

The confusion surrounding the works of this artist precludes the possibility of a more precise attribution than is given here, but it should be noted that No. 183 is a portrait of high quality and superior to the preceding picture. For a discussion of the attributions to Corneille de Lyon, cf. Martin Davies, *National Gallery Catalogues, French School*, 1946, pp. 29–30.

184 JEAN FOUQUET, c. 1420–c. 1481

St. Michael Slaying the Dragon (*Plate IXa*)

Gouache on vellum, $6\frac{1}{8} \times 4\frac{5}{8}$ in.

COLL: no record of provenance before acquisition by Maggs, London, in 1923, from whom it was bought by Lord Bearsted the same year.

LIT: P. Durrieu, *Livre d'Heures peint par Jean Fouquet . . . le 45me Feuillet*, Paris, 1923, pp. 31f., repd.; Trenchard Cox, *Jehan Fouquet*, London, 1931, pp. 78–80; H. Martin, *Les Fouquets de Chantilly*, Paris, 1934, p. 17, fig. 45; K. G. Perls, *Jean Fouquet*, London, 1940, p. 73, Pl. 41; G. Ring, *A Century of French Painting*, London, 1949, p. 212, No. 130.

EXH: B.F.A.C., 1923, No. 116; R.A., Winter, *French Art*, 1932, No. 747f (*Commemorative Catalogue*, No. 955); Paris, Palais National des

Arts, *Chefs d'Œuvre de l'Art Français*, 1937, No. 774; Whitechapel, 1955, No. 42 (Pl. XV in catalogue).

The composition, as with the other miniatures in the series, is divided into two parts. In the upper half St. Michael, wearing gilded armour with a cuirass in the form of a cockleshell, holds in his left hand a round shield and in his right a sword which he raises to strike the seven-headed dragon before him; to the left, behind, a double row of angels, those in the lower stage carrying crosses and the foremost holding the saint's helmet; to the right, rocks, where the single head of a second dragon can be seen. (Part of the sky has become obscured as a result of oxidization.)

The lower part of the composition shows scenes in Hell, which are revealed by severing the ground at the feet of St. Michael. Left, the Devil is enthroned in a cavern from which smoke ascends through a fissure in the earth; centre, demons torturing souls of the damned in the flames; and right, the dragon which has been precipitated into the flames.

In the centre of the composition is the device of Etienne Chevalier with the letter 'M', denoting the antiphon of St. Michael. As in the case of the other miniatures (cf. Martin, *op. cit.*, p. 12), No. 184 has been disfigured by the application of a fragment of border illumination of a later date which conceals the opening words of the antiphon, *Michael Archangele, veni in adjutorium populi*.

The scene described above is on the *verso* of the sheet. On the *recto* are sixteen lines of the text of the end of a prayer in latin referring to the illness of King Hezekiah (Isaiah, xxxviii: text transcribed by Durrieu, p. 32) and border illuminations of rose sprigs, birds and blue and gold leaf decoration, together with Etienne Chevalier's cipher. Beneath is the rubric announcing the exercise of devotion: *Anthene de Saint Michel*.

The volume, *Les Heures d'Etienne Chevalier*, of which this is the forty-fifth leaf, was executed for Etienne Chevalier between 1452–60. It was dispersed, probably in the late eighteenth century, and the majority of the leaves are now in the Musée Condé, Chantilly. Since the present miniature was discovered a further two have been found. It is estimated that eleven miniatures, besides the calendar, are still missing.

The attribution to Fouquet rests on the documented *Antiquités Judaïques* (Ring, p. 211, No. 129). For the history of the Chevalier

MS., and the whereabouts of the miniatures, cf. Ring, No. 130.

The pecten form of cuirass worn by St. Michael is a reference to the *Coquille de St. Jacques*, the emblem of the Abbey of Mont St. Michel, which was adopted by Louis XI when in 1469 he founded the Order of St. Michael, and for which Fouquet, as court painter, illuminated the Book of Statutes. In the frontispiece of this work (cf. Ring, No. 133, Pl. 84) which depicts the king presiding over a *chapitre*, a picture of St. Michael shows him wearing what appears to be the same style of cuirass and holding a similar round shield decorated with a cross. Durrieu points out that the 'bouclier rond' was often associated with St. Michael, e.g. by the van Eycks in the Ghent altarpiece (the figure of St. Michael on the music-stand in the panel with the Singing Angels). He also notes (p. 33) that in the fifteenth century it was often the custom, as here, to depict kings or princes accompanied by angels bearing their helmets.

The fact that the dragon is shown with seven heads is probably a reference to Revelation xii. 3.

185 FRENCH SCHOOL, c. 1500
See *Unknown, (?)twentieth century* (Position in catalogue follows Greuze)

192–203 FRENCH, last quarter of fifteenth century

A Series of Miniatures from the Story of Mélusine

Gouache on vellum (sizes given individually).

COLL: A. W. M. Mensing sale, Amsterdam, 23 November 1937, lot 6, as by Vérard; date of acquisition by Lord Bearsted unrecorded.

Mélusine, a fairy of French folk-lore, was the legendary founder of the house of Lusignan. The story was originally told by Jean d'Arras, *Chronique de la Princesse*, c. 1387. An edition published in Geneva in 1478 (*L'Histoire de la Belle Mélusine*) is illustrated by woodcuts, the compositions of which in some cases resemble the present series. Where this is so the fact is noted by a reference to '1478 Edn.'. (A facsimile of this book was published in Paris, 1924, ed. W. J. Meyer.)

Unless it is otherwise stated a text in French is to be found on the *versi* of the sheets.

192. Two knights jousting ($6\frac{1}{8} \times 6\frac{1}{8}$ in.: arched top with decorated spandrels). cf. W. W. Skeat, *Romans of Parthenay or Tale of Mélusine*, London, 1866, line 988 (*inter alia*); 1478 Edn., f. CXVII; repd. in 1937 sale catalogue.

193. Geoffrey burning the Abbey of Mallieses ($4\frac{1}{2} \times 6\frac{15}{16}$ in.). Skeat, *op. cit.*, 3291ff; 1478 Edn., f. CXLIX.

194. Raymond begging Mélusine for forgiveness ($5\frac{1}{8} \times 6\frac{1}{8}$ in.). Skeat, *op. cit.*, 3788ff.
194v. Mélusine fainting after Raymond calls her a serpent. Skeat, *op. cit.*, 3543ff; 1478 Edn., f. CLI.

195. Unidentified subject: Interior of a bedroom with three knights standing round a priedieu ($5\frac{3}{8} \times 6\frac{3}{8}$ in.: arched top with decorated spandrels).

196. (?)Mélusine giving instructions before her departure ($4\frac{15}{16} \times 6\frac{7}{8}$ in.). Skeat, *op. cit.*, 3648ff.
196v. Raymond and Mélusine swoon and are believed dead ($4 \times 6\frac{1}{8}$ in., French text above). Skeat, *op. cit.*, 3774ff; 1478 Edn., f. CLIII.

197. Mélusine returns to visit her children ($5 \times 6\frac{1}{16}$ in.). Skeat, *op. cit.*, 4019ff; 1478 Edn., f. CLVIII.

198. Geoffrey discovers the tomb of his grandfather Helmas and the alabaster image of Presine in the enchanted mountain ($5\frac{3}{8} \times 6\frac{1}{8}$ in.). Skeat, *op. cit.*, 4509ff; 1478 Edn., f. CLXIII.
198v. Geoffrey entering the opening in the mountain where the giant Grimold guarded Helmas and his daughters ($1\frac{13}{16} \times 6\frac{3}{16}$ in.: top part of a composition; French text above). Skeat, *op. cit.*, 4446ff; 1478 Edn., f. CLXII.

199. Geoffrey rescuing the prisoners after slaying the giant Grimold ($4\frac{1}{16} \times 6\frac{5}{16}$ in.: arched top with decorated spandrels). Skeat, *op. cit.*, 4719ff.

200. The giant Grimold transported in a cart ($3\frac{7}{8} \times 6\frac{1}{8}$ in.). Skeat, *op. cit.*, 4796ff; 1478 Edn., f. CLXV.

201. The Earl of Forest slain by Geoffrey ($6 \times 6\frac{1}{16}$ in.: arched top with decorated spandrels). Skeat, *op. cit.*, 4900ff; 1478 Edn., f. CLXVI.

202. The King of Armenia greeted by the old man in white at the gates of Sparrowhawk Castle ($4\frac{1}{16} \times 6\frac{1}{16}$ in.). Skeat, *op. cit.*, 5419ff; repd. in 1937 sale catalogue.

203. The King of Armenia and Melior in Sparrowhawk Castle ($4\frac{7}{8} \times 5\frac{7}{8}$ in.). Skeat, *op. cit.*, 5532ff; 1478 Edn., f. CLXXXVII.

203v. The death of the King of Armenia ($3\frac{1}{2} \times 6\frac{1}{16}$ in.: French text below). Skeat, *op. cit.*, 5644ff; 1478 Edn., f. CLXXXIX.

These miniatures have hitherto been ascribed to the *atelier* of Antoine Vérard (1450–1519: publisher and illustrator in Paris). The present attribution is due to Dr. Pächt, who from an examination of the photographs regarded them as the product of some French workshop in the last quarter of the fifteenth century, but could not support the specific attribution to Vérard.

186 JEAN-BAPTISTE GREUZE, 1725–1805

The Head of a Girl

Panel (Walnut), $17\frac{3}{4} \times 15$ in.

COLL: according to the San Donato sale catalogue the picture was bought at Baron de Monville's sale in 1839. The only recorded sale of this owner (cf. Lugt, *Catalogue de Ventes*, 1953, No. 14603) was on 7–10 March 1837, when nine pictures were disposed of (sale not checked). Prince Anatole Demidoff, San Donato sale, 26 February 1870, lot 123: bt. by Earl of Dudley; privately sold by this owner in 1923 and acquired shortly afterwards by Lord Bearsted.

LIT: C. Mauclair, *Jean-Baptiste Greuze* (catalogue by J. Martin and C. Masson), Paris, 1905, p. 36, No. 520.

EXH: R.A., Winter, 1871, No. 389.

ENGRAVED: by Doisi, 1845 (lithograph); C. J. L. Courtry (for San Donato sale catalogue).

RELATED PICTURES: *La Prière du Matin* (see below). A head and shoulder version, close to the present picture, is in the Kaiser Friedrich Museum, Berlin (No. 494c). Anita Brookner, 'Jean-Baptiste Greuze', *Burlington Magazine*, XCVIII, June, 1956, p. 196, mentions another at Montpellier and a variant in the National Gallery, Edinburgh (No. 437). A type entitled *Innocence* also closely resembles this composition.

Head and shoulders to right, head turned to left, looking upwards and over her left shoulder; her hair falls over her shoulders and she wears a loose white shift with a mauve cloak across her arms.

The picture was formerly catalogued as *La Volupté* (San Donato sale). It is in fact one of a number of versions of *La Prière du Matin* (Musée Fabre, Montpellier) cut down to a bust length study. Dr. Brookner gives a date for the present picture of *c.* 1786–94, but remarks on the difficulty of placing accurately the many reduced versions which Greuze painted of his own works.

187 JEAN-BAPTISTE GREUZE, 1725–1805

A Child with an Apple

Panel (Walnut), $15\frac{1}{4} \times 12\frac{1}{4}$ in.

COLL: Prince Nicolas Demidoff; by inheritance to his son, Prince Anatole Demidoff and sold by him, San Donato sale, 26 February 1870, lot 116: bt. by Earl of Dudley; privately sold by this owner in 1923 and acquired shortly afterwards by Lord Bearsted.

LIT: C. Mauclair, *Jean-Baptiste Greuze* (catalogue by J. Martin and C. Masson), Paris, 1905, p. 32, No. 453.

EXH: R.A., Winter, 1871, No. 392.

ENGRAVED: by Samuel Cousins, R.A., 1782, *A Golden Pippin* (cf. A. Whitman, *Samuel Cousins*, London, 1904, No. 195); E. Hédouin (for San Donato sale catalogue).

RELATED PICTURES: among a number of versions are ones belonging to the Rt. Hon. R. A. Butler; Cognac sale, Paris, 14 May 1952, lot 16; Lady Janet Douglas-Pennant, Penrhyn. The original was said (cf. Goncourts, *L'Art du XVIe Siècle*, Paris, 1906, vol. II, p. 93) to have been owned by La Live de Jully (later E. W. Lake collection). A variation on the theme of a child with an apple is in the National Gallery (No. 1020).

Head and shoulders to left, head turned towards the spectator, wearing a white dress with a green ribbon in the hair, both arms resting on a table covered with a green cloth, on which is placed an apple on a slice of bread.

The sex of the child is difficult to determine. Formerly entitled *La Petite Boudeuse*, but catalogued by Martin and Masson as *Enfant à la Pomme ou le Petit Boudeur*. The type has also been called *Le Petit Orphelin*. Dated by Dr. Brookner *c.* 1790–95.

189 JEAN-BAPTISTE GREUZE, 1725–1805

A Girl lying in Bed

Canvas, $14\frac{3}{4} \times 18$ in.

COLL: according to Smith (*infra*) the picture belonged to Smith Owen of Condover in 1829.

The provenance is amplified in the Upton catalogue where the names of subsequent owners Lord Owernston [sic], 1864, and R. Cholmondeley of Condover Hall, Shrewsbury, are added. Mauclair (infra) records the ownership of Smith Owen and Lord Overstone.

At the death of William Smith Owen of Condover in 1863 his estates devolved upon his cousin, Thomas Cholmondeley, who died the following year and was succeeded by his brother, Reginald Cholmondeley (d. 1896). The *Young Girl* by Greuze (size, 15 × 18 in.), lent by Reginald Cholmondeley to exhibitions in 1868 and 1871 (see below) may be the present picture. The ownership of Thomas Jones Loyd, later 1st Lord Overstone (d. 1883) has not been confirmed and the picture is not included in the catalogue of part of his collection (*Pictures at Overstone Park*) published in 1877. Sometime later it came into the possession of Lord Dudley, by whom it was sold privately in 1923, and soon afterwards was acquired by Lord Bearsted.

LIT: Smith, 1837, vol. VIII, p. 421, No. 76; C. Mauclair, *Jean-Baptiste Greuze* (catalogue by J. Martin and C. Masson), Paris, 1905, p. 54, No. 830.

EXH: (?) B.I., 1865, No. 79; probably Leeds, 1868, No. 2928; R.A., Winter, 1871, No. 118. (All lent by R. Cholmondeley: entitled *A Young Girl* in the two latter exhibitions (sizes tally) and *The Surprise* in the former (no size given).

ENGRAVED: by F. Joubert (as *Morning*).

Head and shoulders, lying on her left arm on a pillow towards the right, looking up, her right hand on her head; she wears a blue ribbon in her hair and a piece of drapery crosses her right arm above the elbow.

Dated *c.* 1800 by Dr. Brookner, who points out that the picture was wrongly entitled *Nina* (in the Upton catalogue) in confusion with *Nina, ou la Folle par Amour*, a work now only known through a copy by Claude Hoin at Dijon. It was catalogued as *Jeune Fille* by Martin and Masson and by Smith as 'girl about fourteen years of age'. Although the latter describes the picture accurately the size is given as 'about 20 × 26 in.'.

190 JEAN-BAPTISTE GREUZE, 1725–1805

A Girl holding a Spaniel (*Plate VIIIc*)

Panel (Walnut), 18¼ × 15 in. (oval).

COLL: Prince Nicolas Demidoff; by inheritance to his son, Prince Anatole Demidoff and sold by him, San Donato sale, 26 February 1870, lot 112: bt. by Earl of Dudley; privately sold by this owner in 1923 and acquired shortly afterwards by Lord Bearsted.

LIT: C. Mauclair, *Jean-Baptiste Greuze* (catalogue by J. Martin and C. Masson), Paris, 1905, p. 35, No. 505.

EXH: R.A., Winter, 1871, No. 398.

ENGRAVED: by A. Morse; E. Hédouin (for San Donato sale catalogue).

RELATED PICTURE: for a variant, cf. Smith, VIII, p. 419, No. 68. Smith, who imported this picture, alleges that it came from the St. Victor collection. There was only one Greuze of the subject in that sale (Lebrun, Paris, 26f. November 1822, lot 529) which must therefore have been Smith's picture and not as hitherto supposed the one now at Upton. (The San Donato sale catalogue contains no reference to a St. Victor provenance for lot 112 and it appears that Martin and Masson were the first to catalogue Lord Dudley's picture—i.e. the Upton picture—as having belonged to St. Victor. Martin and Masson evidently combined the two pictures in one entry, the present one from the San Donato and Dudley collections and Smith No. 68 from the St. Victor collection.)

In 1956 Smith's picture was on the London market (repd. *Burlington Magazine*, XCVIII, 1956, *Advertising Supplement*, Pl. VII). The same size and shape as No. 190, it portrays the girl looking to the left. She wears a white scarf across her shoulders, as described by Smith and in the St. Victor catalogue (in the present picture the girl is wearing yellow). Martin and Masson give an equivocal description of the dress in their No. 505.

Head and shoulders to right, her head turned towards the spectator over her right shoulder, a small frightened spaniel, only the head of which is seen, clasped in her arms against her chin, her arms resting on a mauve and blue cushion; she wears a yellow dress, a blue ribbon in her hair, a green one falling across the cushion.

Dated *c.* 1786 by Dr. Brookner. This is one of many variations on the theme of a child holding a dog, the subject of which was first exhibited at the Salon in 1769. The exhibited picture is now in Lord Bearsted's private collection at Upton.

191 JEAN-BAPTISTE GREUZE, 1725–1805

Le Matin

Panel (Walnut), $17\frac{3}{4} \times 14\frac{3}{8}$ in. (oval).

COLL: Prince Nicolas Demidoff; by inheritance to his son, Prince Anatole Demidoff and sold by him, San Donato sale, 26 February 1870, lot 113: bt. by Earl of Dudley; privately sold by this owner in 1923 and acquired shortly afterwards by Lord Bearsted.

LIT: C. Mauclair, *Jean-Baptiste Greuze* (catalogue by J. Martin and C. Masson), Paris, 1905, p. 34, No. 486.

EXH: R.A., Winter, 1871, No. 397.

ENGRAVED: by A. Morse; Doisi (lithograph, 1845); C. J. L. Courtry (for San Donato sale catalogue); F. Joubert, 1876.

RELATED PICTURE: Martin and Masson mention a copy in the Walferdin sale, lot 24 (3 April 1888).

A young girl seated in a chair, head and shoulders to left, her head turned over her left shoulder to face the spectator; she wears a white scarf knotted round her head, a white dress, and blue scarf below her shoulder.

Dated *c.* 1800 by Dr. Brookner. In her opinion the attribution is questionable and she suggests that it may be one of the late works painted by the artist's daughter, Anna. The previous cataloguing of this as an autograph work is followed here. The assumption is that its quality is reasonable enough for it to be included among the numerous uneven repetitions of his pre-Revolutionary pictures that Greuze was turning out in order to earn a livelihood at the end of the century.

185 UNKNOWN, (?) twentieth century

The Madonna and Child with Angels

Panel (Poplar), $21\frac{1}{2} \times 15\frac{1}{8}$ in.

COLL: a label on the back reads as follows: *Faisant partie de la Collection du Marquis de Beaulieu sous le No. 19 du Catalogue de la Vente 1837* (the sale is not recorded by Lugt, *Catalogue de Ventes*). There are also two indistinct *Douanes Françaises* labels. The picture was with Dowdeswell in 1918 (cf. Reinach, *infra*); date of acquisition by Lord Bearsted unrecorded.

LIT: S. Reinach, *Répertoire des Peintures*, Paris, 1918, vol. IV, p. 480, repd.; P. Jamot,

'Two Pictures in the French Art Exhibition', *Burlington Magazine*, LX, 1932, p. 173, repd.

EXH: B.F.A.C., 1928, No. 33; R.A., Winter, *French Art*, 1932, No. 71a (*Commemorative Catalogue*, No. 13); Birmingham Art Gallery, *Art Treasures of the Midlands*, 1934, No. 271; Whitechapel, 1955, No. 47.

The Virgin, wearing a blue robe over a crimson dress, her hands clasped in prayer, is seated with the Child on her lap; around her are the winged heads of five child-angels, with a decoration of bayleaves at each side.

Listed by Reinach as Piedmontese or Lombard and catalogued as *French School, c. 1500* in the above exhibitions. Jamot regards it as French, despite the Italian elements which he notices; he remarks that Friedländer concurs with him in this.

Because of its suspiciously strange combination of styles the picture was sent for technical examination at the Courtauld Institute in 1956. In his report Mr. Rees-Jones stated that he found nothing about it which would uphold the attribution to the fifteenth century. The texture and thickness range of the paint is neither that of Italian nor Flemish fifteenth-century painting. The craquelure follows the grain of the wood but paint has been applied thinly after its formation; practically nothing would remain were this repaint to be removed. These arguments in themselves would not preclude the picture from being an unfinished early work. (The alternative possibility, that it is a worn and damaged fragment, can be discounted as the radiograph gives no indication of any but minor losses.)

However, the painting is technically exceptional in having a thick and brittle layer of white lead tempera over the whole surface (chalk ground). White-lead layers have been reported in fifteenth-century pictures under specific colours, generally blue, but they are commonly found in nineteenth-century pictures, particularly in the work of the Pre-Raphaelites. The Courtauld Institute undertook experiments which proved that such a layer would produce an artificial craquelure corresponding to the grain of the wood.

The assumption is that No. 185 is a forgery. According to Rees-Jones it is unusual to find a fake of this quality before 1918 (the date when it was apparently first published).

192–203 VERARD, (Atelier of)
See *French, Last quarter of fifteenth century*

204 ANTOINE VESTIER, 1740–1824

The Artist's Wife

Gouache on ivory, $8\frac{1}{2} \times 6\frac{3}{8}$ in.

COLL: Heine collection, which was bought *en bloc* by Pierpont Morgan; the latter's sale, Christie's, 27 June 1935, lot 657: bt. by Martin for Lord Bearsted.

LIT: G. C. Williamson, *Catalogue of Collection of Miniatures of Pierpont Morgan*, London, 1908, vol. IV, No. 559, Pl. CXC.

Full length, standing, facing, a small knife in her right hand with which she is cutting a monogram on the trunk of a tree at the left of the picture; she wears a white dress trimmed with lace and violet ribbons, and a high white lace cap with violet ribbons and white ostrich feathers on her powdered hair; right, a trellis and urn, and a little white dog at her side.

Marie Ann, daughter of Antoine Révérend, an enameller in Paris, married Antoine Vestier.

The German School

211 HANS HOLBEIN THE YOUNGER, 1497/8–1543

A young Man with a Pink (*Plate VIIIb*)

Panel (Oak), $4\frac{7}{8} \times 4\frac{3}{4}$ in. (almost circular.)

DATED: *ANNO 1533*

COLL: noted as having been in the Jäger collection, Vienna, by Waagen (see below) in 1860. For remarks on this collection, cf. Frimmel, 1891, *infra*, pp. 281–93. Its founder was Franz Jäger (d. 1839) and his eldest son Anton inherited a part of it. The association of the present picture with lot 57 in the Franz Jäger sale (Vienna, 17–18 December 1841)—cf. catalogue entry, R.A., 1950—may therefore be incorrect (sale catalogue not checked) since it belonged to Anton Jäger in 1860. By 1866, when Waagen published his *Vornehmsten Kunstdenkmäler*, the picture was owned by F. J. Gsell; his sale, Vienna, 14 March 1872, lot 208. By 1891 (cf. Frimmel, *infra*) it had passed to Fräulein Gabriele Przibram, Vienna; thence by descent to Frau L. Goldschmidt-Przibram and sold at Amsterdam, 17 June 1924, lot 2, repd. Date of acquisition by Lord Bearsted unrecorded.

LIT: G. F. Waagen, *Die Vornehmsten Kunstdenkmäler in Wien*, Vienna, 1866, vol. I, p. 317; A. Woltmann, *Holbein und seine Zeit*, Leipzig, 1868, vol. II, p. 154, No. 261; T. Frimmel, *Kleine Galeriestudien*, Bamberg, 1891, p. 293; P. Ganz, *Holbein (Klassiker der Kunst)*, 1912, pp. 104 (repd.), 241; T. Frimmel, *Lexikon der Wiener Gemäldesammlungen*, Munich, 1913, vol. II, p. 95, No. 208; p. 278, No. 57; A. B. Chamberlain, *Hans Holbein the Younger*, London, 1913, vol. II, pp. 57, 349; H. A. Schmid, *Hans Holbein der Jüngere*, Basle, 1948, vol. II, p. 367; P. Ganz, *The Paintings of Hans Holbein the Younger*, London, 1950, p. 244, No. 77, Pl. 118.

EXH: Brussels, Hôtel Goffinet, *La Miniature*, 1912, No. 855a; R.A., Winter, *Holbein and other Masters*, 1950, No. 198; Whitechapel, 1955, No. 52; Manchester Art Gallery, *German Art*, 1961, No. 110.

RELATED PICTURES: a copy is mentioned by Woltmann as being in the Hanover Gallery.

This must refer to No. 151 in the 1905 *Catalogue*, which as described appears to represent a different subject.

Bust, facing slightly left, wearing a black cloak open at the neck showing a red vest and white linen shirt, a flat black cap, holding a pink in his right hand. Blue background.

Described by Woltmann as a self portrait, and by Schmid and Ganz as more probably the portrait of a member of the Steelyard Corporation of German merchants of the Hanseatic League in London.

212 Attributed to MICHAEL PACHER, *c.* 1435–1498

Saint George and the Dragon (*Plate Xc*)

Panel (Softwood, with canvas backing), $21\frac{1}{4} \times 15\frac{3}{4}$ in.

COLL: Andreas Colli, Innsbruck (according to Upton catalogue). In 1937 it appears to have been with an 'English dealer' (catalogue of *Gotik in Tirol* exhibition, Innsbruck, 1950: cf. entry No. 96). It was probably acquired by Lord Bearsted soon after 1937.

EXH: Whitechapel, *Five Centuries of European Painting*, 1948, No. 31a; Whitechapel, 1955, No. 49 (Pl. XVIII in catalogue).

COMPANION PICTURES: the present picture has affinities with a half-length figure of St. Barbara, with a gold background, also from the Colli collection and now in the Vienna Museum (No. 1822). C. L. Kuhn, *Pantheon*, XV, 1935, p. 174, published a St. Catherine from the Schniewind collection, New York, which he supposed to be the wing of an altarpiece, *vis-à-vis* the St. Barbara mentioned above. In *Pantheon*, XVIII, 1936, p. 303, W. Suida published another half-length figure of a saint, St. Florian (Fröhlich collection, Vienna), similar to the St. Catherine in having a dark background. He argued, since the St. Barbara has a background of gold, that the SS. Catherine and Florian were the outside wings of an altarpiece, that the St. Barbara was the right inside and that '. . . Aufzufinden wäre noch die ehemalige

Innenseite des linken Flügels, die vielleicht wieder einen männlichen Heiligen darstellt und sicher Goldgrund besitzt'.

It is possible that No. 212 fulfils these conditions, although the integration of the four panels is not wholly convincing. Their sizes are: St. George, 51×46 cm.; St. Barbara, 54×41 cm.; St. Florian, 54×41 cm.; St. Catherine (apparently cut down), 46×44 cm. E. Hempel, *Das Werk Michael Pachers*, Vienna, 1943, reproduces the St. Barbara (Pl. 88) as by Pacher, and mentions the St. Catherine (p. 29, No. 88, under entry for St. Barbara) which he regards as belonging to the circle of Friedrich Pacher. The St. Barbara was exhibited in 1950 at Innsbruck (*Gotik in Tirol*, No. 96). In the catalogue it was listed as a not fully authenticated work and was connected with a St. George (English dealer, 1937). In the same entry it was suggested that the 'external' saints mentioned above, SS. Florian and Catherine, were by a different hand.

The present panel, which has been built-up at the back, is only 4 mm. thick, including gesso layer. This suggests that at some period it has been divided, and supports the hypothesis that the St. George formed the shutter of an altarpiece with another painting on the reverse.

St. George stands half length, looking down at the exiguous dragon into which he thrusts his sword; he wears armour and a green cloak thrown over his shoulders; an ornamental band encircles his forehead, from which his hair falls to his shoulders; in his mailed left hand he grasps a staff or lance, while his right is raised, gripping the sword. Gold background.

Previously catalogued as by Michael Pacher. The qualification of this attribution in the present catalogue is partly on the basis of the picture's probable connection with the panels mentioned above, about which the authorities quoted show some scepticism. Nevertheless, No. 212 is an impressive painting and, if not by Pacher himself, must be by an able follower.

213 Workshop of BERNHARD STRIGEL, 1460/1–1528

The Emperor Maximilian I

Panel (Lime or Poplar), 15½×11⅞ in.

COLL: Mrs. E. M. Renshaw sale, Sotheby's, 16 December 1942, lot 89, as by Strigel: bt. by Arcade Gallery, from whom it was acquired by Lord Bearsted, c. 1945.

EXH: Whitechapel, 1955, No. 51 (Pl. XVII in catalogue); Manchester Art Gallery, *German Art*, 1961, No. 45.

RELATED PICTURE: a similar portrait, apparently also a workshop product, is in the Louvre.

Head and shoulders, facing half right, seated before a window; on the wall, left, are green brocade hangings; he wears a crimson velvet hat and crimson cloak with brown lapels edged with green over an orange tunic embroidered in black; round his neck hangs the order of the Golden Fleece; his hands are held across his chest and in one of them is a folded paper on which can be read part of a petition: . . . *Ich armer dienstman bitt von meiner (?)erjagten Frau wegen von euer Rat und helfft als* . . . An old inscription on the back of the panel records: *Inscrizione trova . . . antica cornice nei Davanti. Maximilianus Rex Romanorum.*

Maximilian (1459–1519), son of Frederick III and Eleanor of Portugal, crowned Emperor of the Holy Roman Empire in 1508, married in 1477 Mary, daughter and heiress of Charles the Bold, Duke of Burgundy.

The portrait has up to now been catalogued as by Strigel, but it does not appear to possess the quality of an autograph work.

214 WOLGEMUTH (?)

See *Younger Master of the Schotten Altarpiece*

214 YOUNGER MASTER OF THE SCHOTTEN ALTARPIECE, active last quarter of fifteenth century

The Martyrdom of St. Barbara

Panel (Pine), 29×21¾ in.

COLL: Canon Sutton sale, Christie's, 12 February 1926, lot 35, as by Wohlgemuth: bt. by Warner; date of acquisition by Lord Bearsted unrecorded.

LIT: Otto Benesch, 'Der Meister der Krainburger Altars', *Wiener Jahrbuch*, VII, 1930, p. 189, Pl. 55a; E. Panofsky, *Albrecht Dürer*, Princetown, 1948, vol. I, p. 17; vol. II, fig. 3.

EXH: Whitechapel, 1955, No. 50; Manchester Art Gallery, *German Art*, 1961, No. 38.

COMPANION PICTURE: the relationship to a panel of the same measurements depicting *St. Barbara beaten by her Father* in the City of York Art Gallery (Lycett-Green Bequest) was first pointed out by Michael Jaffé. This repeats the figures of the saint and the king in the present picture and is clearly by the same hand and from the same series or altarpiece (the action in both pictures takes place in the same direction).

The saint, wearing red robes, kneels in prayer in the foreground of a rocky landscape while her father, Dioscurus, in brightly coloured clothes, stands behind her grasping her hair in his left hand, a sword raised in his right with which he is about to decapitate her; right, two men look on, the foremost of whom wears an embroidered robe edged with fur and a patch over his right eye; in the distance is a village on a hill.

Formerly catalogued as by (?) Wolgemuth but attributed by Benesch to the Younger Master of the Schotten altarpiece or to a close follower. Benesch considers that it shows an advance in pictorial handling over the 'Mary' panels of c. 1475 (see below). Panofsky catalogues the picture as by the Younger Master of the Schotten Altarpiece, although in the first edition of his monograph on Dürer (1945) it was attributed to the workshop of Wolgemuth.

The master derives his name from the High Altar of the Schottenkirche, Vienna. Benesch distinguishes two hands in the execution, the Elder Master who was responsible for the Rogier-like Passion scenes on the outside of the double wings of the altarpiece, one of which is dated 1469, and the Younger Master, who painted the slightly later (c. 1475) inner scenes from the life of Mary in which the influence of the Nurnberg school and of Wolgemuth is apparent. It is the latter hand that Benesch associates with the present picture.

The title of the incident is taken from Benesch. The subject was described in the Upton catalogue and by Panofsky as the *Decollation of St. Dympna* but it is more likely to represent St. Barbara. The existence of the York panel further supports this identification.

The picture was probably part of an altarpiece. The thickness of the panel ($\frac{3}{4}$ in.) confirms that it is unlikely to have been divided and that therefore there was never anything painted on the reverse.

The Italian School

221 BELLOTTO

See *Riva, N.L.A. de la (Attributed to):* under Spanish School

222 CANALETTO (ANTONIO CANALE), 1697–1768

Bacino di San Marco, Venice

Canvas, 55¼ × 90½ in.

COLL: Countess Mniszech (according to Sedelmayer Gallery catalogue); W. Benoni White sale, Christie's, 23 May 1879, lot 68, as by Guardi: bt. by Sedelmayer; E. Sécrétan sale, Paris, 1 July 1889, lot 104; with Sedelmayer; Duke of Marlborough by 1898; Duchess of Marlborough sale, Christie's, 7 June 1918, lot 125: bt. by Colnaghi; with Knoedler, from whom bought by W. Salomon, New York, 1919; with Davis; with Duveen, from whom acquired by Lord Bearsted.

LIT: *Sedelmayer Gallery Catalogue*, 1898, p. 220, repd.; D. Sutton, 'The Bearsted Collection', *Country Life*, CXVII, 1955, p. 871; W. G. Constable, *Canaletto*, London, 1962, vol. II, No. 144, repd.

EXH: Whitechapel, 1955, No. 65.

RELATED PICTURES: (I) A similar but less extensive view of about the same date was recently acquired by the National Museum of Wales, Cardiff. (II) Constable lists a doubtful work in the collection of the Earl of Malmesbury.

A panoramic view looking towards the Doge's Palace and embracing the whole of the Venetian waterfront, bounded on the left by the entrance to the Canal della Giudecca and the Dogana, on the right by the steps and part of the façade of S. Giorgio Maggiore, and on the waterfront by the campanile of S. Zaccaria. Numerous gondolas and some *bissone* are collected round the Piazzetta, where the Doge's galley is moored; left the bows of a warship, anchored in the canal; right a frigate firing, and in the foreground market boats and gondolas. The view is more extensive than the eye could include in a single focus and the artist probably made use of a *camera obscura*.

Francis Watson suggests that the scene may represent the Feast of the *Assunta* at the moment when the Doge has departed for the Lido in the *Bucintoro*, normally moored alongside the Piazzetta, but not visible here. Indeed Redford (*Art Sales*, 1888, vol. I, p. 298) mentions a *View of Venice with the Procession of the Marriage of the Adriatic* (included in the Benoni White sale as a *View of Venice* by Guardi) which although somewhat over-perspicaciously described, can only refer to the present picture. Since it was this early style of Canaletto that Guardi was to emulate, it is perhaps understandable that the picture was once attributed to the latter artist.

Constable dates the picture c. 1725–26. Sutton is perhaps over-critical in doubting the attribution.

223 CARLO CRIVELLI, active 1457–1493

Two Apostles

Panels (Poplar). Each 12½ × 9¼ in. (rectangular panels with painted surfaces forming arched tops, with gesso and priming in spandrels; additions or joins 2 in. from bottom.)

COLL: G. Cornwall Legh (said to have been bought by this owner—cf. Rushforth, *infra*, p. 96—from Vallati in Rome at about the same time, i.e. 1859, that the National Gallery, London, acquired from him part of the same altarpiece, the *Dead Christ supported by Two Angels*); with Colnaghi; date of acquisition by Lord Bearsted unrecorded.

LIT: G. Carter, *Catalogue of Paintings at High Legh*, 1890, Nos. 66, 67 (as by Mantegna); G. Rushforth, *Crivelli*, London, 1900, pp. 47–48, 96; L. Venturi, *Le Origine della Pittura Veneziana*, Venice, 1907, pp. 197–8; J. A. Crowe and G. B. Cavalcaselle, *History of Painting in North Italy*, London, 1912, vol. I, p. 90 (note 2); A. Venturi, *Storia dell'Arte Italiana*, Milan, 1914, vol. VII(3), p. 360; L. Testi, *La Storia della Pittura Veneziana*, 1915, vol. II, pp. 611, 672; F. Drey, *Crivelli*, Munich, 1927, pp. 53–55, 126; R. van Marle, *Development of the Italian Schools of Painting,*

The Hague, 1936, vol. XVIII, p. 13; P. Zampetti, *Carlo Crivelli nelle Marche*, 1952, pp. 26–33; B. Berenson, *Venetian Pictures of the Renaissance*, London, 1957, p. 70.

EXH: Whitechapel, 1955, No. 58.

The two half-length figures are framed together. The young man on the left, almost facing the spectator, wearing an olive-green robe with blue and white cloak, is reading from a scroll; the elderly man on the right, reading a book, wears a white robe and green cloak and faces slightly to the left. Gold backgrounds (regilt).

The two panels are said to be part of the *predella* of the altarpiece from the Church of the Franciscans at Montefiore dell'Aso, near Fermo, which was dismembered during the Napoleonic Wars (Rushforth, *op. cit.*, p. 47). Six other *predella* panels from the same series which were at High Legh and also came from Vallati have been dispersed as follows:

Clark Institute, Williamstown: *Christ*. Honolulu Academy of Arts: *St. Andrew*; *Apostle with a Book* (called St. Jerome). Detroit Museum: *St. Peter*; *Apostle writing in a Book* (called St. John). Lehman collection, New York: *Apostle with a Scroll*.

(The two panels at Upton have been described as St. John the Evangelist and St. Luke. This is difficult to substantiate and the writing Apostle at Detroit is more likely to be the St. John of the series.)

The tooling of the haloes of these eight figures is consistent.

Three *predella* panels with half-length Apostles have also been associated with the same altarpiece:

Proehl collection, Amsterdam: *St. Andrew*. Castello Sforzesco, Milan: *St. Bartholomew*; *Apostle with a Book* (called St. John).

These do not conform exactly to the Legh series and are regarded by Martin Davies (*National Gallery Catalogue: Earlier Italian Schools*, 1951, pp. 119–20) as belonging to a different series. Two further panels of *Christ* and *St. Peter*, which may be connected with those at Milan, were in the Marinucci collection, Rome (cf. W. Suida, *Apollo*, XX, 1934, p. 122, repd.) and are now at El Paso Museum, Texas, and at Yale respectively. They are regarded by Suida as being later than the Montefiore series.

For the most recent reconstruction of the Montefiore altarpiece, cf. Zampetti, *op. cit.*, p. 31. This embodies a full-length *Virgin and Child* and a *St. Francis* in the Brussels Museum (bought from Vallati in 1862), the National

Gallery *Pietà* mentioned above, three full-length and three half-length figures, formerly in the Franciscan Church and now in St. Lucia, Montefiore, and a half-length figure in the Lanz collection, Amsterdam. The *predella* is said to comprise thirteen panels and includes five with Colnaghi (i.e. those formerly in the Legh collection), two at Detroit, two in the Castello Sforzesco, one in the Lehman and one in the Proehl collection.

However the Proehl *St. Andrew* repeats one of the figures in the Legh series and cannot therefore belong to the same *predella*. The two Castello Sforzesco saints, as already suggested, also appear to belong to another series, the existence of which is further confirmed by the stylistically related Marinucci panels (not mentioned by Zampetti), which again repeat figures in the Legh set. It is reasonable to suppose that these five panels, which are more vigorously painted than those formerly in the Legh collection, were part of the *predella* of a second altarpiece, probably slightly later than the Montefiore polyptych. It is not necessary to assume that the full complement of Apostles were included in the *predella* (for this point cf. Martin Davis, *op. cit.*, who cites the Ascoli altarpiece, the *predella* of which contains Christ and ten Apostles, the remaining two being included in the main tier) but it is likely that an even number of Apostles were depicted.

The Montefiore altarpiece has generally been dated *c.* 1472, when the artist may have been living at Fermo (cf. Rushforth). The present panels are consistent with this date.

224 DOSSO

See *Sustris*

236 Follower of FRA FILIPPO LIPPI, *c.* 1406–1469

Three Acts of Charity (*Plate XIc*)

Panel (Poplar), $9\frac{1}{4} \times 28\frac{1}{2}$ in.

COLL: previous history unrecorded but in the possession of Lord Bearsted by 1924.

EXH: B.F.A.C., 1924, No. 7; Whitechapel, *Five Centuries of European Painting*, 1948, No. 28; Whitechapel, 1955, No. 56 (Pl. XX in catalogue).

Three successive scenes viewed through the arches of a cloister: left, the righteous man hands drink to Christ as the unknown stranger; centre, he hands Him food; and right, he offers

Him rest. In the first and second episodes attendant figures carry wine and bread. The subject is taken from Our Lord's description of the Last Judgement, Matthew xxv. 34–40.

Part of a *predella*. In the Upton catalogue as School of Masaccio with the qualification that it is probably the work of Filippo Lippi. Dr. Friedländer, who saw the picture in 1936, is recorded as having thought it nearer Filippino, while Sir Kenneth Clark is quoted in the 1955 Whitechapel catalogue as suggesting an attribution to the artist responsible for a group of pictures which Berenson described as between Neri di Bicci and the Master of the Carrand Triptych.

No. 236, however, while very close to Fra Filippo, seems in so far as can be judged in its damaged state to be by the hand responsible for two *predella* panels in the Johnson collection, Philadelphia, for which Berenson (*Catalogue of the Johnson Collection*, 1913, pp. 17–19) suggested the Master of the Castello Nativity. For Berenson's reconstruction of this artist, see *ibid*, No. 23.

In *Rivista d'Arte*, XVII, 1935, pp. 411f., M. Salmi identifies these two *predelle* as miracles of St. Justus and St. Clement, attributing them to the Master of the Castello Nativity and associating them with an altarpiece of the *Madonna and Saints* in SS. Giusto e Clemente, Faltugnano, which was published by U. Procacci, *ibid*, pp. 405–11, fig. 1, and attributed to the same master. This altarpiece, with its rather elaborate architectural background of arches set at right angles to one another, seems to indicate a similar artistic approach to the present painting.

225 FLORENTINE, fifteenth century

See *Verrocchio (Follower of)*

233 FLORENTINE, late fifteenth century

The Madonna and Child with an Angel

Panel (Pine), $18\frac{5}{8} \times 14\frac{3}{4}$ in.

COLL: according to the Upton catalogue, Count Ingenheim, Silesia; Marcel van Nemes (cf. *Bulletin of Bachstitz Gallery*) who owned it in 1925, the year in which it was bought by Lord Bearsted.

LIT: G. Gronau, 'A Madonna by Filippino Lippi' (published with letter in support from M. J. Friedländer), *Bulletin of Bachstitz Gallery*,

The Hague, 1925, IX/X, pp. 102–4, repd.; R. van Marle, *Development of Italian Schools of Painting*, The Hague, 1931, vol. XII, p. 359, note 2; A. Scharf, *Filippino Lippi*, Vienna, 1935, p. 116, No. 127, Pl. 125.

EXH: Munich, Alte Pinakothek, 1923–24; Whitechapel, 1955, No. 59 (Pl. XXI in catalogue).

The Madonna, wearing a red robe and dark green cloak, stands in an open landscape; she bends forward to receive the Child from an angel, dressed in pale blue, who kneels at the left; in the distance is a town on a lake.

Van Marle and Gronau, followed in the Upton catalogue, give the picture to Filippino, while Scharf regards it as by an unknown follower. It is not included in Neilson's 1938 monograph on the artist. Berenson is quoted in the Bachstitz Gallery *Bulletin* as having attributed it to Amico di Sandro, and Sir Kenneth Clark, in the Whitechapel exhibition catalogue, as suggesting a late work from the Botticelli workshop. Gronau dates the picture at about the time of the Esther *cassone* panels (i.e. *c.* 1480).

The problem of attribution is aggravated by the poor condition of the picture (the Child, the angel's head, etc., are considerably retouched). A picture resembling it in composition and to some extent in handling, to which the name of Cosimo Rosselli has been attached, is in Palazzo Venezia, Rome.

[Note: Berenson, *Florentine Pictures*, 1963, p. 191, Pl. 1017, as Cosimo Rosselli.]

226 GIOTTO

See *Master of the Fabriano Altarpiece*

227 GIOVANNI DI PAOLO, active 1420–1482

The Presentation of the Virgin (Plate XIa)

Panel (Poplar), $8\frac{1}{8} \times 10\frac{5}{8}$ in. (including gold, strip of $\frac{1}{8}$ in. at each side; top and bottom probably cut.)

COLL: anonymous sale, Christie's, 24 February 1922, lot 38, as Florentine School: bt. by Smith; by 1923 in the possession of Mrs. Otto Kahn; in 1937 with the Bachstitz Gallery, The Hague, and acquired by Lord Bearsted the same year.

LIT: *Bulletin of the Metropolitan Museum, New York*, XVIII, 1923, p. 108; A. Scharf, *Unknown Masterpieces* (ed. Valentiner), London,

Plate XIa Giovanni di Paolo (227)

Plate XIb Master of Fabriano Altarpiece (226)

Plate XIc Follower of Filippo Lippi (236)

Plate XIIa Guardi (228)

Plate XIIb Paret (257)

1930, No. 5; J. Pope-Hennessy, 'A Predella Panel by Giovanni di Paolo', *Burlington Magazine*, LXXI, 1937, pp. 108–9, repd.; J. Pope-Hennessy, *Giovanni di Paolo*, London, 1937, pp. 53 (note 87), 171.

EXH: Metropolitan Museum, New York, *The Arts of the Italian Renaissance*, 1923, No. 11; on loan to the National Gallery, London, 1937–46; Whitechapel, *Five Centuries of European Painting*, 1948, No. 17; Whitechapel, 1955, No. 57 (frontispiece in catalogue); R.A., Winter, *Italian Art and Britain*, 1960, No. 290.

RELATED PICTURES: an earlier *predella* panel dependant on the fresco at S. Leonardo al Lago (see below) but with some affinities to No. 227 is in the Pinacoteca at Siena (No. 174); the lost *Presentation* which must have formed part of the same *predella* as the two scenes of the *Life of the Virgin* in the Doria collection may have been related.

The interior of a temple, enclosed on either side by panelled walls, with a paved floor in the foreground and six slender columns; a broad flight of steps in the centre leads to the golden tabernacle, before which stands Zacharias and a second priest, right, and the young Virgin, wearing a pale blue dress flecked with gold, left. The Virgin turns to St. Anne, who, attended by two fashionably dressed women and wearing a blue robe, stands on the lowest step at the left. Opposite and facing her at the foot of the steps is Joachim; behind him can be seen a male figure, and above, on a level with the tabernacle, a group of children, forming a choir.

Part of a *predella*. Pope-Hennessy (note 87) draws attention to the iconographical interest of the present picture in that the attendant figures from the left side of Gentile da Fabriano's *Presentation of Christ* in the Louvre (the right-hand portion of the *predella* of the S. Trinità altarpiece) are here inserted into the conventional *Presentation of the Virgin* composition. In the *Burlington Magazine* he elaborates the genesis of the composition, noting the influence of the Pseudo-Pellegrini di Mariano's *Presentation of the Virgin* of c. 1425 in the Vatican Gallery (No. 238) for the architectural features, and the fresco (attributed to Lippo Vanni) of the same subject in the church of S. Leonardo al Lago near Siena (probably deriving from the lost Lorenzetti fresco painted for the Ospedale della Scala at Siena) which supplies a precedent for the group of onlookers. Bartolo di Fredi in a *Presentation* in

the Kress collection, New York, with compositional analogies to No. 227, uses the same motif. Pope-Hennessy dates the present picture c. 1445–50, i.e. approximately coeval with Giovanni di Paolo's large *Presentation of Christ* at Siena (No. 211) of 1447–48.

228 FRANCESCO GUARDI, 1712–1793

Pope Pius VI blessing the People of Venice

Canvas, $19\frac{7}{8} \times 26\frac{1}{4}$ in.　　　　(*Plate XIIa*)

COLL: D. P. Sellar sale, Paris, 6 June 1889, lot 33; Walter Burns; date of acquisition by Lord Bearsted unrecorded, but still referred to as being in the Burns collection in 1929 (cf. *Pantheon, infra*). A label inscribed with what appears to be the name *M. J. Stewart-Mackenzie, (?)Florence, Feb 1879* is attached to the back of the stretcher.

LIT: G. A. Simonson, *Guardi*, London, 1904, pp. 44, 94; K. Lange, 'Guardis Segenspendung Papst Pius VI', *Münchner Jahrbuch*, VI, 1911, p. 279; G. A. Simonson, 'Guardi's Pictures of the Papal Benediction', *Burlington Magazine*, XXXVI, 1920, pp. 93–94; T. Borenius. 'Il Contributo dell'Inghilterra alla Mostra di Palazzo Pitti', *Dedalo*, III, 1922–23, pp. 99, 104, repd.; G. Fiocco, *Guardi*, Florence, 1923, pp. 36, 72, No. 71, Pl. LX; V. Ojetti, L. Dami, N. Tarchiani, *La Pittura Italiana del Seicento e del Settecento*, Rome, 1924, p. 153, repd.; M. Nugent, *Alla Mostra della Pittura Italiana del 600 e 700*, 1924, p. 169; K. Erdmann, 'Zwei neue Historienbilder von Guardi', *Pantheon*, IV, 1929, pp. 506–9; M. Goering, *Guardi*, Vienna, 1944, pp. 61–62, 85, No. 140 Pl. 140; V. Moschini, *Guardi*, Milan, 1952, Pl. 158; R.A., Winter, *European Masters of the 18th Century*, 1954, No. 92 (catalogue entry relating to Ashmolean version).

EXH: R.A., Winter, 1886, No. 154; B.F.A.C., 1919, No. 4; Palazzo Pitti, Florence, *Pittura Italiana del Sei–Settecento*, 1922, No. 515; Whitechapel, *Five Centuries of European Painting*, 1948, No. 20; Whitechapel, *Eighteenth Century Venice*, 1951, No. 35; Whitechapel, 1955, No. 66 (Pl. XXIV in catalogue).

ENGRAVED: by F. Milius (for Sellar sale).

RELATED PICTURES: three other versions of this scene are known: in the Ashmolean Museum, Oxford (No. 149); in the Dresden Gallery (No. 601a); and in the Stuttgart Gallery (No. 548). The two latter are practically identical in size with the Upton picture;

the Ashmolean version is slightly larger ($24\frac{3}{4} \times 31\frac{1}{2}$ in.). More restricted views, showing the benediction loggia, are in the Kress collection, Washington, the Modiano collection, Bologna (Moschini, *op. cit.*, Pl. 160) and ex-collection Comte Gerard de Loriol, which was sold at Sotheby's, 29 June 1959, lot 63. A further painting of the subject was sold by Doucet, 5 June 1912, lot 159.

RELATED DRAWINGS: (I) Mrs. Ryland sale, Sotheby's, 26 June 1957, lot 11, now in the E. Korner collection, London; (II), (III) Exhibited at Galerie Cailleux, *Tiepolo et Guardi dans les Collections Françaises*, 1952, Nos. 88, 89, the former without figures.

Goering (*op. cit.*, p. 62) tentatively associates a drawing of figures seen from behind (Metropolitan Museum, New York) with No. 228. For a discussion of this and other *macchiette*, see No. 229.

A large crowd is gathered in the Campo SS. Giovanni e Paolo, surrounding the Pope, who addresses the populace from a specially erected *macchina* in front of the Scuola di San Marco. Right, the Colleoni monument and part of the church of SS. Giovanni e Paolo.

'In 1782 [21 May], Pietro Edwards, an English painter who had recently been appointed inspector of public paintings to the Republic, commissioned Guardi to execute four paintings recording various episodes during the Pope's official visit to Venice between May 15th and 19th of that year . . . Guardi, who often adapted his compositions from the works of others seems to have based [this painting] on an engraving by Jacopo Leonardis after Domenico Fossati, a hack work probably rushed out to take advantage of the popular interest aroused by the Pope's visit' (cf. Whitechapel, 1951 exhibition catalogue).

The three other episodes painted by Guardi in this series are: (1) *The Doge meeting the Pope at the Island of S. Giorgio in Alga*. A painting of this subject in the Rossello collection, Milan, is reproduced by Goering, No. 139. (2) *The Te Deum sung in the Pope's honour in SS. Giovanni e Paolo*. Pictures in the Groult collection, Paris, and Cleveland Museum, Ohio. (3) *The Pope receiving in Audience the Doge and Signoria in the Convent of SS. Giovanni e Paolo*. Pictures in the Mond collection, London, and Cleveland Museum, Ohio. The fourth and final scene is the one represented by the present picture. An explanation for the existence of additional versions of this last episode was given by Simonson (*Burlington Magazine*)

when he advanced the theory that this was the picture with which Guardi made the greatest impression and which he was called upon to multiply.

It is generally agreed that the Ashmolean picture belongs to the original series commissioned by Edwards and that this included the Groult and Mond versions of episodes (3) and (4) respectively. The three pictures are of almost identical size and differ from the others mentioned above in being slightly larger. The set was evidently repeated by Guardi in a second and smaller series which may have comprised the Cleveland pictures and either No. 228 or one of the versions. While opinions differ in the literature quoted above as to the respective merits of these versions (Fiocco regarded the Stuttgart and Dresden pictures as eighteenth-century copies), it should be emphasized that the present painting is an autograph work of high quality. A discussion as to the composition of this second series would in any case be polemical.

229 FRANCESCO GUARDI, 1712–1793

A Study of a Crowd seen from Behind

Pen and brush and black ink and wash on stone coloured paper. $4\frac{5}{8} \times 9\frac{3}{4}$ in.

COLL: H. Oppenheimer in 1911; his sale, Christie's, 10 July 1938, lot 92; given to Lord Bearsted by Sir Alec Martin, 1938.

LIT: J. Byam Shaw, *Drawings of Guardi*, London, 1951, p. 72 (under catalogue entry No. 51).

EXH: B.F.A.C., *Venetian Painting of the 18th Century*, 1911, No. 83; Whitechapel, *Five Centuries of European Painting*, 1948, No. 21; Whitechapel, *Eighteenth Century Venice*, 1951, No. 47; Whitechapel, 1955, No. 67; Fondazione Cini, Venice, *Canaletto e Guardi*, 1962, No. 93.

A group of full-length standing figures seen from behind, mostly wearing cloaks and three-cornered hats.

The drawing was included by Byam Shaw (*op. cit.*) under catalogue entry for a related sheet of *macchiette* in the Metropolitan Museum, New York, where other similar sheets were mentioned. It is also extremely close to two such drawings in the Boymans Museum, Rotterdam (published by Byam Shaw in *Art Quarterly*, XVII, 1954, pp. 274–6, figs. 1, 2). In the catalogue of the 1962 exhibition Byam Shaw associates both these and the present drawing with the picture of the *Doge in the*

Bucintoro setting out for the Lido at Tolosa (Fiocco, No. 57, Pl. LVI), in which the spectacle is watched by groups of figures lining the shore. The Tolosa painting belongs to the series depicting incidents relating to the election of the Doge which was engraved by Brustolon after Canaletto and copied in oils by Guardi. Comparable *macchiette* to No. 229 are likely to have been used as studies for this series.

The suggestion that this drawing is connected with the preceding painting appears to be unlikely.

230 FRANCESCO GUARDI, 1712–1793

The Dogana, Venice

Canvas, 16⅜ × 26⅛ in.

COLL: Lord Foley sale, Ruxley Lodge, 14 October 1919: lots 594, 595, *Views of Venice* by Guardi, refer to this and the following picture; Otto Gutekunst; with Knoedler, 1921, from whom it was acquired by Lord Bearsted.

RELATED DRAWINGS: two drawings in the Wallraf-Richartz Museum are very close in composition to the present picture and to No. 231 (cf. W. Kronig, 'Zeichnungen von Guardi in Köln', *Wallraf-Richartz Jahrbuch*, XVIII, 1956, pp. 244ff, Pls. 187, 193, where related paintings are also reproduced).

COMPANION PICTURE: No. 231.

A view with the Dogana in the centre, S.M. della Salute at the extreme right, and in the distance to the left the Church of the Redentore on the Giudecca; gondolas and sailing vessels.

Although this and No. 231 have been made into companion pictures they differ in style (the present work is perhaps superior) and are unlikely to have been painted as a pair.

231 FRANCESCO GUARDI, 1712–1793

S. Giorgio Maggiore, Venice

Canvas, 16½ × 26¼ in.

COLL: as No. 230.

RELATED DRAWING: cf. No. 230.

COMPANION PICTURE: No. 230.

The Church and Island of S. Giorgio Maggiore, left, with the point of the Giudecca seen on the right beyond the Canale della Grazia; gondolas and sailing boats.

Cf. No. 230.

232 ITALIAN SCHOOL

See *North Italian (c. 1300)*

233 LIPPI, FILIPPINO

See *Florentine (late fifteenth century)*

234 LOMBARD, *c.* 1470

Illuminated Initial "S"

Vellum, 7⅞ × 7⅞ in. (to border: the decoration extends ⅛ in. beyond on each side).

COLL: according to the Upton catalogue from Stift Seitenstaetten, Austria, and thence K. W. Bachstitz, The Hague. Date of acquisition by Lord Bearsted unrecorded.

EXH: Whitechapel, 1955, No. 55.

The Holy Family appears within a scroll decoration of pale blue, green and pink, with stylized pomegranates, some of which are continued beyond the border. The Child stands on a table in the centre, wearing a white embroidered smock; He is supported by the Virgin, left, and St. Joseph, right; St. Anne stands beside the Virgin. Gold background.

A cutting from a choral book or other manuscript which was catalogued previously as Lombard School, fifteenth century, probably by Foppa. According to Dr. Otto Pächt who gave his opinion after seeing a photograph, the relationship to Foppa is a very distant one. Dr. Pächt's attribution is followed here.

235 LORENZO LOTTO, *c.* 1480–1556

A young Dominican Monk (*Plate Xd*)

Panel (Poplar), 12⅝ × 10 in.

COLL: first discovered by G. Glück, *c.* 1910, in the collection of Count Leo Pininsky, Lemberg and before 1926 (cf. article by Venturi in *L'Arte* of that year) owned by Stefan von Auspitz, Vienna, where it was described by Fröhlich Bume in 1932; with the Bachstitz Gallery, The Hague, by 1935 and acquired at some unspecified later date by Lord Bearsted.

LIT: G. Glück, 'Ein neugefundenes Jugendwerk Lorenzo Lottos', *Kunstgeschichtliches Jahrbuch der K. K. Zentral-Kommission*, IV, 1910, p. 215, fig. 52 (reprinted by Glück, *Aus drei Jahrhunderts Europäischer Malerei*, Vienna, 1933, pp. 268–87); A. Venturi, 'Un Ritratto di Lorenzo Lotto', *L'Arte*, 1926, pp. 246–7, repd.; *idem, Studi dal Vero*, Milan, 1927, pp. 264–7, fig. 166; *idem, Storia dell'Arte Italiana*, Milan, 1929, vol. IX (4), p. 113; L. Fröhlich-Bume, 'Sammlung Auspitz-Wien', *Pantheon*, X, 1932, p. 399; B. Berenson, *Italian Pictures of the Renaissance*, Oxford, 1932, p. 312; *Bulletin of the Bachstitz Gallery*, The Hague, 1935, pp. 9–10; A. Banti and A. Boschetto, *Lorenzo Lotto*, Florence, 1953, p. 68, No. 20, Pl. 44; L. Coletti, *Lorenzo Lotto*, Bergamo, 1953, p. 37, No. 12 (mentioned under entry referring to *Portrait of a Woman*, Dijon Museum); A. Morassi, 'The Lotto Exhibition in Venice', *Burlington Magazine*, XCV, 1953, repd. p. 293; B. Berenson, *Lorenzo Lotto*, London, 1955, p. 5, Pl. 10; *idem, Venetian Pictures of the Renaissance*, 1957, p. 106.

EXH: Venice, Palazzo Ducale, *Lotto*, 1953, No. 26 (repd. in catalogue); Whitechapel, 1955, No. 60.

Head and shoulders, body facing slightly left, head turned towards the spectator, wearing a creamy-white robe and black cap. Dark green background.

Dated by Venturi (1929), 1500–3; by Boschetto, *c.* 1508. P. Zampetti, who also dates the picture *c.* 1508, recalls (catalogue of Lotto Exhibition, Venice) the suggestion that the sitter may be one of the friars of the Monastery of Recanati, near which the artist lived from 1506–8. Berenson (1955) dates the picture *c.* 1506 and draws attention to the fact that the sitter is the same as a saint, seen in profile, in the Asolo altarpiece of 1506 (repd. by Berenson, Pls. 12, 15): 'Lotto possibly took this monk as a model (i.e. for the Asolo altarpiece) or he may have painted it just before. Having his face still fixed in his visual memory he may have reproduced it unconsciously, as occurs not infrequently, though in ways not often so patent.'

236 MASACCIO (School of)

See *Filippo Lippi (Follower of)*

226 MASTER OF THE FABRIANO ALTARPIECE, active mid-fourteenth century

The Last Supper (*Plate XIb*)

Panel (Poplar), 9⅛ × 42 in.

INSCRIBED: *HOC OPVS FECIT FIERI DOMINA GIOVANNA VXOR OLIM*

GIANNI DE BARDIS PRO REMEDIO ANIME ISSIVS GIANNI MAGISTER IOCTI DE FLORENTIA.

COLL: the altarpiece of which this panel was part of the *predella* is said to have been transferred from S. Maria di Ricorboli (near Florence) to S. Gregorio in Piazza de' Mozzi, Florence (now destroyed), in 1528. It was on the high altar of the latter church in 1554 (see below), but had probably been replaced sometime before 1661 by the effigy of *St. Gregory* painted by Francesco Curradi (d. 1661). It is possible that it was removed from the church when the building was modernized, but this must anyhow have been before 1775 when it was secularized and the monks were forced to leave (cf. Paatz, *Kirchen von Florenz*, Frankfurt a.M., 1941, vol. II, p. 382). The *Last Supper* alone was in the collection of Princess Orloff, 1875 (cf. Crowe and Cavalcaselle, *infra*); Prince Orloff sale, Paris, 29 April 1920, lot 29, repd.; with Knoedler, 1923, and acquired by Lord Bearsted the same year. On the back of the panel is an unidentified seal with a monogram, and a Florentine export seal.

LIT: Codice Magliabechianus-Strozzi, cl. XXVI, 170, *Sepolture in Diverse Chiese della Città e Contado di Firenze*, f. 160 (seventeenth-century MS. in Biblioteca Nazionale, Florence); G. Vasari, *Le Vite* (ed. Milanesi, 1878), p. 401, note; J. A. Crowe and G. B. Cavalcaselle, *Storia della Pittura in Italia*, 1875, vol. I, pp. 586–7, and 1903 (English edn.), vol. II, p. 111; H. Thode, *Giotto*, Leipzig, 1899, p. 140; I. B. Supino, *Giotto*, Florence, 1920, vol. I, p. 270; G. Soulier, *Les Influences Orientales dans la Peinture Toscane*, Paris, 1924, p. 99, note 2; B. Berenson, 'Quadri senza Casa', *Dedalo*, XI, 1931, pp. 974–7, repd. p. 970; B. Nicolson, 'Whitechapel Art Gallery', *Burlington Magazine*, XC, 1948, p. 82; R. Offner, *Corpus of Florentine Painting*, New York, 1956, Sec. III, vol. VI, p. 127, note 19; vol. VIII, pp. 169–73, repd.

EXH: B.F.A.C., 1923, No. 106; Whitechapel, *Five Centuries of European Painting*, 1948, No. 16; Whitechapel, 1955, No. 53 (Pl. XIX in catalogue).

Our Lord, distinguished by the blue mantle which He wears, is seated at the left end of a long table, with St. John kneeling before Him, resting his head on His lap; the other disciples are seated along the far side of the table, which is covered by a white cloth. The moment depicted is when Christ has spoken the words:

'But, behold, the hand of him that betrayeth me is with me on the table.' The reaction of Judas is to raise his hands in protest. Offner points out that the halo of St. Peter is incomplete, and that the picture may have had a narrow strip removed from the top and left.

The attribution to the Master of the Fabriano altarpiece is due to Offner, who mentions the picture in vol. VI of his *Corpus* and catalogues it fully in vol. VIII. He suggests that on iconographic grounds the *Last Supper* was the *predella* beneath a *Crucifixion*. Offner has also traced the history of the altarpiece, which is referred to in the Magliabechianus MS. as follows: *S. Gregorio su la Piazza de' Mozzi* ... *L'Anno 1554 nell'Altare maggiore di d. a Chiesa nella tavola vi era scritto quanto sotto: 'Hoc opus fecit fieri Dna Giovanna uxor olim Gianni de Bardis pro remedio anime ipsius Gianni.' La qual tavola alcuni in quel tempo dicevano che l'anno 1528 fu levata dalla chiesa di S. Maria di Ricorboli* ...

According to Offner the inscription is authentic but cannot be by the painter of the present panel nor can it originally have been in its present position. The donatrix may be the wife of Giovanni di Vieri dei Bardi, who died in 1355, a date which accords with the period of the panel (cf. Passerini, *Genealogia e Storia della Famiglia Bardi*, 1846, Tav. XIV: MS. in Biblioteca Nazionale, Florence). The portion of the inscription naming Giotto appears to be a later addition, though such phrasing need imply no more than a workshop product (in the present instance a fault of grammar gives *magister* instead of the genitive, *magistri*).

No. 226 is linked to the late style of Giotto. References to the picture are as follows: Crowe and Cavalcaselle (1875)—by Giotto; the same authors, 1903—'painted very much in Giotto's manner'; Milanesi—by Giotto; Thode—inscription doubtful; Supino—workshop of Giotto; Soulier—ascribed to Taddeo Gaddi, perhaps preparatory to the S. Croce fresco; Berenson—by Bernardo Daddi; Upton catalogue—by Giotto.

For the life of the Master of the Fabriano altarpiece, associated with the *bottega* of Daddi, *c.* 1340, cf. Offner, Sec. III, vol. V, pp. 141-51.

[Note: Berenson, *Florentine Pictures*, 1963, p. 58, as Studio of Daddi.]

232 NORTH ITALIAN, *c.* 1300

Illuminated Initial "D"

Vellum, $6\frac{1}{16} \times 6\frac{1}{2}$ in. (size of sheet).

COLL: A. W. M. Mensing sale, Amsterdam, 23 November 1937, lot 10; date of acquisition by Lord Bearsted unrecorded.

EXH: Whitechapel, 1955, No. 54.

Eleven apostles in blue, orange, pink and grey robes, with SS. Peter and Paul seated in the centre, grouped within the initial; the Holy Ghost is represented as light breaking through clouds. Gold background.

A cutting from a choral book or other manuscript. Previously catalogued as Italian School, *c.* 1400, the present attribution is due to Dr. Otto Pächt (opinion after seeing a photograph).

237 NORTH ITALIAN, *c.* 1550

An unknown Man

Slate, $12\frac{7}{8} \times 7\frac{1}{4}$ in.

COLL: Sir Francis Cook, 4th Bart.; with Agnew, 1945, from whom acquired by Lord Bearsted.

LIT: T. Borenius, *Catalogue of the Cook Collection (Italian Schools)*, London, 1913, vol. I, No. 98, repd.; L. Fröhlich-Bume, 'Some unpublished Portraits by Parmigianino', *Burlington Magazine*, XLVI, 1925, p. 88, Pl. 11f; G. Copertini, *Il Parmigianino*, Parma, 1932, vol. I, p. 223, note 27; B. Nicolson, 'Whitechapel Art Gallery', *Burlington Magazine*, XC, 1948, p. 82; A. O. Quintavalle, *Il Parmigianino*, Milan, 1949, p. 204; S. J. Freedberg, *Parmigianino*, Cambridge (Mass.), 1950, p. 232, Pl. 163.

EXH: B.F.A.C., 1912, No. 21; Whitechapel, *Five Centuries of European Painting*, 1948 (omitted from catalogue); Whitechapel, 1955, No. 62.

A young man, head and shoulders, facing half towards the left, wearing a scarlet jacket with white collar edged with gold and white fur over his shoulders. The cramped composition seems to indicate that the thin slate on which the portrait is painted may have been reduced in size, possibly for reasons of condition: the head is badly damaged and the whole of the shadowed portion of the face at the right has been repainted.

Attributed to Parmigianino by Borenius and Fröhlich-Bume. Copertini regards it as a work belonging to the mid-sixteenth century or later, and notes that the sitter appears among a collection of miniatures (now in the gallery at Parma) which belonged to the Farnese family, who did not arrive in Parma until 1545. Nicolson finds the attribution to Parmigianino unconvincing and suggests that it is by an Italian mannerist painter before 1550. Quintavalle attributes it to Niccolò dell'Abate. Freedberg opposes the attribution to Parmigianino on stylistic grounds and further points out that none of the artist's authentic work is painted on slate, which was only used on rare occasions until later in the century. In the Upton catalogue the picture passed under the name of Parmigianino. The attribution to Niccolò dell' Abate seems to deserve consideration.

237 PARMIGIANINO

See *North Italian (c. 1550)*

224 LAMBERT SUSTRIS, 1515/20–c. 1595

The Rape of Proserpine

Panel (Pine: planed down and built up at edges), $11\frac{3}{4} \times 27$ in. (including addition of 1 in. at bottom).

COLL: Lady Horner (perhaps inherited from her grandfather, William Graham) until 1943 when according to the Upton catalogue it was acquired by Lord Bearsted. On the reverse of the panel is the export seal of the Accademia of Venice.

LIT: B. Berenson, *Venetian Pictures of the Renaissance*, London, 1957, p. 168.

EXH: Whitechapel, 1955, No. 61 (Pl. XXII in catalogue).

In a romantic landscape Proserpine struggles with Pluto in a golden chariot drawn towards the right by two white horses. (*Pentimenti* in area of horses heads and forelegs.)

In the Upton catalogue, supposedly following Berenson (*North Italian Painters*, 1907, p. 209), as by Dosso Dossi, but qualified by the comment that Sir Kenneth Clark believed it to be by Bordone. It is clearly not by Dosso and Prof. Waterhouse has pointed out that this attribution arose from a confusion with another picture of the same subject in the collection of Lady Horner, which is still at Mells and was bought in at a sale at Christie's, 17 June 1949, lot 19 (exhibited, R.A., Winter, 1960, No. 56). This is by Dosso and is the picture listed by Berenson.

The present attribution, which is convincing, is taken from Berenson's 1957 lists.

238 DOMENICO TIEPOLO, 1727–1804

The Madonna appearing to St. Anthony of Padua and St. Francis of Paula (*Plate Xa*)

Canvas, $39 \times 23\frac{7}{8}$ in. (arched top and irregular shaped base).

COLL: Lord Battersea (d. 1907) in 1894. Date of acquisition by Lord Bearsted unrecorded.

LIT: B. Berenson, *Venetian Painters of the Renaissance*, London, 1902, p. 133; E. Sack, *Giambattista and Domenico Tiepolo*, Hamburg, 1910, p. 226, No. 547; D. Sutton, 'The Bearsted Collection', *Country Life*, CXVII, 1955, p. 871.

EXH: New Galleries, London, *Venetian Art*, 1894, No. 204; Whitechapel, 1955, No. 64.

ENGRAVED: by Domenico Tiepolo: etching in reverse, inscribed *Jo Bapta inv: et pin: Dom: Filius del et in.* (cf. A. de Vesme, *Le Peintre-Graveur Italien*, Milan, 1906, pp. 407–8, No. 56; repd. by Sack, *op. cit.*, Pl. 156).

RELATED PICTURE: Sack (p. 166, No. 141) catalogues a sketch by G. B. Tiepolo (size, 40×24 cm.), untraced after the Pauwels sale in Paris in 1877, which he relates to the etching. This sketch, like No. 238, is in the reverse direction to the etching. Sack's catalogue entry for the Upton picture was presumably based on Berenson's description, for he lists it merely as *Madonna and Saints* and connects it neither with his No. 141 nor with the etching.

The Madonna appears seated on a cloud, wearing red and blue robes, holding the Child who stands at her knee, attended by an angel, behind, and two winged angel heads, left. St. Francis kneels in profile at the right, a breviary and bundle in front of him, his staff resting against his right shoulder; behind is his attribute of a sun with the letters *TAS* visible (the final letters of the word *Charitas*). St. Anthony stands at the left behind the Madonna, reading his breviary, a sprig of lily on the steps in front of him. Architectural background and behind the Madonna a green marble column and maroon curtain.

Formerly attributed to G. B. Tiepolo, but regarded by Mr. Francis Watson (oral communication) as a work of Domenico. It would be usual, he suggests, for Domenico to copy his father's picture, rather than to paint from the engraving, and this would account for the picture being in the same direction as Sack

No. 141, supposedly the original by Giambattista, and in the reverse direction to the etching. Sutton also considered the picture to be by Domenico.

238 TIEPOLO, G.B.

See *Tiepolo, Domenico*

239 TINTORETTO (JACOPO ROBUSTI), 1518–1594

The Wise and Foolish Virgins (*Plate VIa*)

Canvas, $31\frac{3}{4} \times 38\frac{1}{4}$ in.

COLL: Robert Napier of Shandon sale, Christie's, 13 April 1877, lot 394, as by Veronese: bt. by Cox; anonymous sale, Sotheby's, 18 May 1938, lot 74: bt. by Buttery, from whom acquired by Lord Bearsted.

LIT: J. C. Robinson, *Catalogue of the Works of Art of Robert Napier*, London, 1865, No. 342 (as by Veronese); B. Berenson, *Venetian Pictures of the Renaissance*, London, 1957, p. 178 (as by Tintoretto).

EXH: Whitechapel, 1955, No. 63 (Pls. XXIII, XXV in catalogue); R.A., Winter, *Italian Art and Britain*, 1960, No. 55.

RELATED PICTURES: a variant is in the collection of D. G. van Beuningen, Vierhouten, Holland (cf. D. Hannema, *Catalogue of the van Beuningen Collection*, Rotterdam, 1949, No. 102, Pl. 145). Another is in the Johnson collection, Philadelphia (cf. B. Berenson, *Catalogue*, 1913, vol. I, No. 211: catalogued as School of Tintoretto, but with the name of Palma Giovane suggested).

The bridegroom, attended by the five wise virgins, leans from a balcony above a hall or courtyard and addresses the five foolish virgins who appeal for admission from below; to their left is a kitchen and in the background a double colonnade, surmounted by arms with *palle*, where three figures are visible; above, two rooms open from the balcony, a ballroom in the centre with dancing couples, and left, a dining room where a servant is laying a table; two musicians stand at the extreme right of the balcony. (*Pentimenti* in paved floor.)

The unusual iconography of this scene (Matthew xxv. 11) is made explicit in the van Beuningen version where a foolish virgin carries a banderole on which is written, 'Signore, Signore, apretici', and a wise virgin carries another inscribed 'In verita vidicho io non vi conochio'.

The present picture is dated 1548 by Berenson. Pallucchini (*La Giovinezza del Tintoretto*, Milan, 1950, p. 110, fig. 173) omits the Upton picture but dates the van Beuningen version 1547–48. He considers that the Johnson version is a studio work. In this context he cites the passage in Ridolfi (*Maraviglie*, ed. von Hadeln, vol. II, p. 15) where Tintoretto is stated to have made small puppets and placed them in perspective settings. It seems likely that such a construction was used in No. 239.

225 Follower of ANDREA DEL VERROCCHIO, *c.* 1435–1488

The Madonna and Child (*Plate Xb*)

Panel (Poplar), $29\frac{7}{8} \times 20\frac{5}{8}$ in.

COLL: according to Knoedler, who acquired the picture from Langton Douglas in 1918, it had formed the altarpiece of the chapel at Duxhurst, Reigate, the home for female inebriates founded by Lady Henry Somerset, who had removed the picture from Eastnor Castle or Reigate Priory for this purpose. Formerly it had belonged to her father, the 3rd Earl Somers (1819–83), and may have been among the pictures he bought in Italy during the second half of the century. It was sold by Knoedler to Lord Bearsted.

LIT: R. van Marle, *Development of the Italian Schools of Painting*, The Hague, 1929, vol. XI, p. 568, fig. 346.

EXH: Whitechapel, *Five Centuries of European Painting*, 1948, No. 69.

The Madonna stands almost three-quarter length before a concave architectural throne of pink stone, with Corinthian pilasters and scarlet frieze and with the tops of cypress trees seen beyond; she wears a pale red dress, dark blue-green robe edged with gold and mauve headdress, and looks down at the Child whom she holds in her arms.

Catalogued by van Marle and in the Whitechapel exhibition as School of Verrocchio, in the Upton catalogue as Florentine, fifteenth century, probably School of Baldovinetti. The influence of Verrocchio is plain and so to some extent is that of Botticelli. It may be by Botticini.

[Note: Berenson, *Florentine Pictures*, 1963, p. 147, as Master of S. Miniato.]

The Spanish School

253 Imitator of FRANCISCO DE GOYA, 1746–1828

Don Francisco Bayeu y Subias

Canvas, $38\frac{1}{2} \times 28\frac{5}{8}$ in.

COLL: previous history and date of acquisition by Lord Bearsted unrecorded, but before 1928.

LIT: D. Sutton, 'The Bearsted Collection', *Country Life*, CXVII, 1955, p. 871; X. de Salas, 'Cronica de Londres', *Goya*, VI, 1955, pp. 365–6 and in *Archivo Español de Arte*, 112, 1955, p. 359 (No. 52), Pl. VIII; J. A. Gaya Nuño, *La Pintura Español fuera de España*, Madrid, 1958, No. 895.

EXH: B.F.A.C., *Spanish Art*, 1928, No. 19; Whitechapel, 1955, No. 40 (Pl. XIII in catalogue).

RELATED PICTURES: two portraits by Goya of this sitter, separated by about eight years, are known. The first, in the Valencia Museum, signed and dated 1786, is almost identical in composition to the present picture (cf. X. Desparmet Fitz-Gerald, *L'Œuvre Peint de Goya*, 1928–50, vol. II, p. 47, No. 328, Pl. 255). What is probably a repetition of this picture belongs to the Marqués de Santillana (repd., A. L. Mayer, *Francisco de Goya*, London, 1924, No. 212a, Pl. 70).

The second, No. 721 in the Prado, Madrid, shows Bayeu seated and is dated by Fitz-Gerald, 1794 (*op. cit.*, No. 357, Pl. 281). Bayeu himself painted a self portrait of a similar composition (repd. V. de Sambricio, *Bayeu*, Madrid, 1955, Pl. 40).

Three-quarter length, body facing half right, head turned towards the spectator, standing before an easel, a brush held in his right hand by his side; he wears a black coat with silver braid in the front and at the cuff, and a white stock; his hair is tied behind with a black bow.

Francisco Bayeu (1734–95), a Spanish painter who worked under Mengs on the decoration of the Royal Palace, was the brother-in-law and master of Goya.

After the Whitechapel exhibition in 1955 doubts were expressed about the authenticity of this picture, which had previously been regarded as an autograph work by Goya, in date between the Valencia and Prado portraits. Sutton questioned the attribution and de Salas mentioned the possibility of it being a mid-nineteenth-century copy. Miss Enriquetta Harris pointed out that it is painted in a style which Goya did not develop until after Bayeu's death.

Despite the competence of the portrait it is difficult to accept the original attribution. Goya's pictures are known to have been copied after his death (e.g. by Fortuny) and indeed a copy by Fortuny of the Prado portrait of Bayeu is recorded (Marquise Landolfo Carcano sale, Paris, 30 May 1912, lot 40, repd.). Although this is no evidence for linking Fortuny's name with No. 253, it can perhaps be regarded as supporting the supposition that the hand of an extremely capable artist, possibly after Goya's death, might have been responsible for it.

254 GOYA

See *Lucas, Eugenio*

255 EL GRECO (DOMENIKOS THEOTOCOPOULOS), 1541–1614

El Espolio (*Plate IXb*)

Panel (Pine), $21\frac{7}{8} \times 13\frac{3}{8}$ in. (including oak fillets added at sides: right, $\frac{1}{2}$ in.; left, $\frac{7}{8}$ in.).

SIGNED: Δ...ΟΣ ΘΕΟΤ...ΥΝΟΣ (on *cartellino*, mostly effaced).

COLL: Don Gaspar de Haro y Guzman, Marquis del Carpio and de Heliche, whose monogram and coronet are on the back of the panel. It is recorded by Barcia (p. 261, note) that Don Gaspar's pictures bore an identifying mark, and in an inventory of the Haro possessions published by Barcia (Appendix I, p. 246) occurs an entry which probably describes the present picture. This reads: 'Otra dicha, companera de la antecedente en el tamano, y del mismo autor, el prendimento de Cristo.' The preceding entry—'Otra pintura en tablo de una vision que tuvo Felipe II, de mano de Dominico Greco, de tres quartas de alto y cerca de media vara de ancho'—refers to the *Dream of Philip II*, now in the National Gallery, ex-collection Stirling of Keir, 1955. This measures 54×35 cm., whereas the present picture without the additions measures 55·5 × 31·1 cm.

Don Gaspar, the son of Luis Mendez de Haro, who succeeded his uncle the Conde Duque of Olivares as chamberlain to Philip IV, was Spanish ambassador at Rome in 1682 and Viceroy of Naples until his death in 1687. Inventories of his collection of pictures were taken in 1682 before his departure for Naples from Rome, and after his death in Naples in 1687. These, together with another of 1669, which was formerly in the Alba archives, have since disappeared. A further inventory of Don Gaspar's paintings, dated June 1651, is preserved among the archives of the Duke of Alba, but it has so far not been possible to consult it in connection with No. 255 (reference is made to this inventory by N. MacLaren, *National Gallery Catalogues: Spanish School*, 1952, p. 77, note 4). The inventory published by Barcia and mentioned above is a copy of an undated list of the pictures belonging to Don Gaspar and to his father Don Luis, which was also found among the Alba archives.

At the death of Don Gaspar his collection of pictures passed to his daughter, Doña Catalina de Haro, who married the 10th Duke of Alba in 1688. An old label on the back of the panel states that the picture was painted for the Duchess of Alba, but there is no evidence of it having been in the possession of the Alba family before 1688.

According to Cossio (see below) the picture later entered the collection of Delacroix and thence became the property of his executor, the artist Baron Schwiter (d. 1889): for Delacroix's admiration of El Greco, cf. X. de Salas, 'La Valoracion del Greco por los Romanticos', *Archivo Español de Arte*, 1940–41, p. 404, where the present picture is mentioned. It was acquired by Chéramy, according to Cossio on the advice of Degas; Chéramy sale, Paris, 5 May 1908, lot 77: bt. by Ducrey; with Wildenstein, 1938 (their records of this period destroyed) and probably shortly afterwards bought by Lord Bearsted.

The statement in Kubler and Soria (see below) to the effect that No. 255 was presented by the artist to Philip II and hung in the Escorial is mistaken. The reference given to F. de los Santos, *Descripción de San Lorenzo del Escorial*, Madrid, 1657, VII (folio 142 *recto* and *verso*, not as stated f. 141) relates only to the large *Adoration of the Name of Jesus* in the Escorial.

LIT: L. Rouart, 'La Collection de M. Chéramy', *Les Arts*, 1907, pp. 6, repd., 10; M. B. Cossio, *El Greco*, Madrid, 1908, pp. 189, 597–8, No. 194; J. Meier-Graefe and E. Klossowski, *La Collection Chéramy*, Munich, 1908, pp. 47–48, No. 21, Pl. 21, A. M. de Barcia, *Catálogo de la Colección . . . Duque de Alba*, 1911, p. 246; A. L. Mayer, *El Greco*, Rome, 1921, p. 11; *idem*, *Domenico Theotocopuli, El Greco*, Munich, 1926, p. 14, No. 73, repd.; *idem*, *El Greco*, Berlin, 1931, p. 48; E. K. Waterhouse, 'El Greco's Italian Period', *Art Studies*, 1930, pp. 73–74, 86, No. 11, repd.; M. Legendre and A. Hartmann, *El Greco*, Paris, 1937, p. 200, repd.; J. Camón Aznar, *Dominico Greco*, Madrid, 1950, vol. I, p. 308; vol. II, p. 1364, No. 150; M. Soria, 'Greco's Italian Period', *Arte Veneta*, VIII, 1954, p. 221; X. de Salas, *Goya*, VI, 1955, p. 366 and in *Archivo Español de Arte*, 112, 1955, p. 359 (No. 52); J. A. Gaya Nuño, *La Pintura Española fuera de España*, Madrid, 1958, No. 1212; G. Kubler and M. Soria, *Art and Architecture in Spain and Portugal, 1500–1800*, 1959, p. 213, note 47.

EXH: R.A., *Greek Art*, 1946, No. 351; Whitechapel, *Five Centuries of European Painting*, 1948, No. 19; Whitechapel, 1955, No. 38 (Pl. XXVI in catalogue).

RELATED PICTURES: No. 255 is a small-scale version of the altarpiece of 1577–79 in the Sacristy of the Cathedral at Toledo, for which an advance payment made to the artist in June 1577 is the first document recording his presence in Spain. A number of other small replicas of varying sizes exist: cf. Camón Aznar, *op. cit.*, II, pp. 1364–5, Nos. 147–9, 151–8; for versions of the top half of the composition only, *ibid*, Nos. 159–62; and for a copy by Jorge Manuel Theotocopoulis in the Prado (No. 832), *ibid*, No. 163.

Christ stands on Calvary in the centre of a group of soldiers, one of whom reaches to tear His robe; in the right foreground an executioner bends over the cross which lies on the ground and pierces holes for the nails; he is watched by the Three Marys standing at the left.

Generally dated *c.* 1580–82, immediately following the altarpiece, except by Waterhouse who regards it as the first version of the subject, placing it as early as 1570. Philip Troutman (oral communication) observes that the greater weight of the figures and their disassociation from the sky (which in this panel is more extensive than in the monumental painting) indicate a slightly earlier date than the altar-piece, in which a unification of figures and space has been achieved. Whether or not it was executed with the cathedral commission in mind, or, since the date of Greco's arrival in Spain is unknown, whether it was painted in Italy or Spain, it is impossible to judge, but in view of its distinguished quality it may well be one of the models, 'originals of all that he had painted in his life', seen by Pacheco on his visit to the artist in 1611 (*Arte de la Pintura*, Bk. III, ch. I).

For the iconography of the subject, cf. J. M. de Azcarate, 'La Iconografia de el Expolio del Greco', *Archivo Español de Arte*, 1955, 111, pp. 189–97.

For an analysis of the composition—the combination of traditional designs of the *Kiss of Judas* and the *Mocking of Christ*, as well as the possible influence of Dürer's engraving of the *Flagellation*—cf. Waterhouse, *op. cit.*, who also notes that the model for the carpenter is the same as for the blind man in Greco's *Healing of the Blind* at Dresden. Certain figures recall Italian prototypes. The portrait-like spectator at the left wearing armour is reminiscent of the equestrian figure, also conspicuous in armour, at the left of Tintoretto's great *Crucifixion* of 1565 in the Scuola di San Rocco. The half seen group of the Three Marys may reflect the huddled figures in the corner of the *Crucifixion of St. Peter* in Michelangelo's Cappella Paolina fresco. And the figure bending over the cross is derived from one of the fishermen in Raphael's tapestry cartoon of *The Miraculous Draught of Fishes*.

254 EUGENIO LUCAS Y PADILLA, 1824–1870

The Sermon

Canvas, $27 \times 20\frac{3}{8}$ in.

COLL: Alphonse Kann, from whom acquired by Agnew, 1921; Walter Burns sale, Christie's, 3 May 1929, lot 28, as by Goya: bt. by Martin for Lord Bearsted.

LIT: anon., 'The Magnasco Society', *Apollo*, II, 1925, pp. 297, 9, repd.; X. de Salas, 'Cronica de Londres', *Goya*, VI, 1955, p. 365 and in *Archivo Español de Arte*, 112, 1955, p. 359 (No. 52); J. A. Gaya Nuño, *La Pintura Española fuera de España*, Madrid, 1958, No. 1615.

EXH: Agnew, London, *Magnasco Society*, 1925, No. 12; Whitechapel, 1955, No. 41 (Pl. XIV in catalogue).

The interior of a church with a priest addressing a congregation from the pulpit; light from the windows behind him floods the scene, which is bounded by curtains of pale crimson and turquoise at the sides and by figures in shadow in the foreground.

The picture was previously attributed to Goya, but it is almost certainly by Lucas. A note in the Whitechapel exhibition catalogue gives the information that Mr. Neil MacLaren believes it to be by this artist. De Salas and Gaya Nuño agree with his opinion.

256 MADRID SCHOOL, early seventeenth century

St. Elizabeth of Hungary

Canvas, $14 \times 11\frac{5}{8}$ in.

COLL: stated to have belonged to Lord Weymouth, but not included in this owner's sale of pictures at Sotheby's, 4 October 1944; with Agnew, 1944, from whom acquired by Lord Bearsted.

LIT: X. de Salas, 'Cronica de Londres', *Goya*, VI, 1955, p. 365 and in *Archivo Español de Arte*, 112, 1955, p. 359 (No. 52), Pl. III; J. A. Gaya Nuño, *La Pintura Española fuera de España*, Madrid, 1958, No. 159.

EXH: Whitechapel, 1955, No. 39.

Nearly half length, body almost facing, head turned to the left and looking up; her right hand held across her breast, her left raised; she wears a crown and the habit of a Franciscan nun.

The picture was formerly catalogued as by (?)Murillo but the relationship is minimal. It was referred to by de Salas under the present heading. It appears to have been cut from a larger picture.

256 MURILLO (?)

See *Madrid School, early seventeenth century*

257 LUIS PARET Y ALCAZAR, 1746–1799

The Quay, Olaveaga (*Plate XIIb*)

Canvas, $26\frac{1}{2} \times 37$ in.

SIGNED: *L P p.*

COLL: anonymous sale, Christie's, 24 March 1922, lot 111: bt. by Sabin and probably acquired by Lord Bearsted soon afterwards. The history of the picture has been confused by association in the literature quoted with one of a pair of paintings noted as being in the Lopez de Calle collection, Bilbao, in 1927.

LIT: J. de Orueta, *Memorias de un Bilbaino*, S. Sebastian, 1929, repd.; J. A. Gaya Nuño, 'Louis Paret', *Boletin de la Sociedad Española de Escursiones*, LVI, 1952, p. 141, No. 20; O. Delgado, *Paret y Alcazar*, Madrid, 1957, pp. 171–2, 251, No. 55, fig. 72; J. A. Gaya Nuño, *La Pintura Española fuera de España*, Madrid, 1958, No. 2146, Pl. 250; G. Kubler and M. Soria, *Art and Architecture in Spain and Portugal, 1500–1800*, London, 1959, p. 302, Pl. 165a.

A number of people are gathered on the quay which is backed by houses and has a tree in the right foreground; on the left, hills slope to the water's edge where various sailing vessels are moored; by the quay are two rowing boats.

Dated by Delgado *c.* 1786 and certainly executed during the period (1780–92) when Paret was living in Northern Spain, painting the harbour views which earned him the title of the 'Spanish Vernet' and designing fountains at Bilbao and Pamplona. Delgado gives incorrect measurements (82 × 120 cm.) for No. 257, thereby relating it in scale to the series of harbour views commissioned by Charles III (1786–92) now in the Palacio Real, Madrid.

Olaveaga is a district of Bilbao lying to the north of the town on the way to Portugalete. No. 257 has been entitled the *Arsenal Quay, Bilbao*, but the description given by Orueta and retained here is more likely to be correct.

221 Attributed to NICOLAS LOUIS ALBERT DE LA RIVA, 1755–1818

A Garden Scene

Canvas, 21¾ × 30⅜ in.

COLL: H. G. Bohn sale, Christie's, 28 March 1885, lot 1489, as a *View of Ranelagh* by Hogarth: bt. by Bantry. (In the catalogue of the Bohn collection, privately printed 1884 [p. 91] it was listed as having been bought privately.) In the Burdett-Coutts collection by 1890; W. Burdett-Coutts sale, Christie's, 4 May 1922, lot 31, as Ranelagh, etc.: bt. by Sabin; date of acquisition by Lord Bearsted unrecorded.

EXH: Guildhall, London, 1890, No. 106; Paris, *Franco-British Exhibition*, 1908, No. 65; Whitechapel, 1955, No. 68.

A lady and gentleman stand conversing by a stone pedestal surmounted by an urn, left, on a grass path which leads between flower beds lined with orange trees to a fence at the end of the garden; beyond it on the right is a villa with a detached garden; at the end of the grass path steps lead up to a small pavilion among trees.

Formerly catalogued unconvincingly as by Bellotto and prior to that quite implausibly as a view of Ranelagh by Hogarth. The present attribution is due to Dr. Dos Santos, to whose notice Mr. Francis Watson brought the picture in the belief that it was by a Portuguese artist. De la Riva was active in Spain from 1792 until 1800, and at Lisbon from 1800 until his death in 1818. It does not seem possible to judge whether this is a Portuguese or Spanish scene.

Index of Changed Attributions

(Instances where only the qualification of an attribution is modified are not included)

Number	Previous Attribution	Present Attribution
British School		
60	Pond	English, *c.* 1745.
67	Romney	Hardy, John.
82	Stubbs	Zoffany, Johann, R.A. (Att. to).
Dutch School		
115	Dutch School	Flinck, Govert.
121	Poelenbergh	Haensbergen, Johannes van.
122	Potter(?)	Meurant, Emanuel.
Flemish and Netherlandish Schools		
145	Bouts, Dirk	Rogier van der Weyden (Follower).
146	Bouts, Dirk	Rogier van der Weyden (Follower).
147	Bouts, Dirk	Master of St. Lucy Legend.
149	Brueghel, Jan the Elder	Brueghel, Pieter (After).
151	Burgundian Follower of Rogier van der Weyden	Master of St. Barbara Legend.
152	Coninxloo, Gillis van	Wtewael, Joachim.
French School		
180	Clouet, Jean (Att. to)	Clouet, François (Atelier).
181	Clouet, Jean (Att. to)	Clouet, François (Atelier).
185	French, *c.* 1500	Unknown, (?) twentieth century.
192–203	Vérard (Atelier)	French, last quarter of fifteenth century.
German School		
214	Wolgemuth	Younger Master of the Schotten Altarpiece.
Italian School		
221	Bellotto	Riva, N. L. A. de la (Att. to): See *Spanish School.*
224	Dosso	Sustris, Lambert.
225	Florentine, fifteenth century	Verrocchio (Follower of).
226	Giotto	Master of Fabriano Altarpiece.
232	Italian School	North Italian, *c.* 1300.
233	Lippi, Filippino	Florentine, late fifteenth century.
236	Masaccio (School of)	Lippi, Fra Filippo (Follower of).
237	Parmigianino	North Italian, *c.* 1550.
238	Tiepolo, G. B.	Tiepolo, Domenico.
Spanish School		
254	Goya	Lucas, Eugenio.
256	Murillo(?)	Madrid School, early seventeenth century.

APPENDIX II

Index of Artists

THE NATIONAL TRUST was founded in 1895 to save fine buildings and countryside which might otherwise be destroyed or spoilt. It preserves them for your enjoyment.

It owns large areas of our coastline, moorland, mountain, common and woodlands. It also owns Roman remains, castles, country houses, and other buildings of architectural and historic value. All of these are open to visitors.

The National Trust is a charity and is independent of the State. To carry on its work it relies on gifts, legacies, and members' subscriptions. As a member of the Trust you also can help to preserve the national inheritance.

Particulars of membership can be obtained from The National Trust, 23 Caxton Street, London, S.W.1.